VICKIE,

THANK YO... NG

MY BOOK.

HOPE YOU ENJOY IT!

STAY STRONG!

WITH GRATITUDE,

Thriving

ISBN: 979-8-218-11403-9

Library of Congress Control Number: 2022922252

Printed in the United States of America.

Interior Design by Crystal Heidel
Interior sketches by: Kathleen Fitzgerald, Ellen Collins, Crystal Heidel, and multiple artists from Freepik.com and Unsplash.com.

Cover art by Kathleen Fitzgerald
First Edition

Thriving

FACING CANCER WITH FAITH, POSITIVITY & SERENITY

KIM KING

This book is dedicated to

My wonderful family who supported and loved me through every step of the journey. A very special thank you to my two sisters who were in touch every day and visited as often as they could.

My amazing and loving friends for their visits, gifts, cards, and wonderful soups and desserts. Special thanks for their prayers, positive thoughts, and remote reiki. You always kept me smiling and entertained.

All of the compassionate and giving Beebe nurses, doctors, technicians and administrative staff who opened their hearts to me and gave me so much more than what they earned in their paychecks. I could never have done it without their incredible caring and am so very grateful to each and every one of them.

My sage and dedicated wife who gave up so much of her life to take me to my doctors' appointments, medical tests, procedures, lab work, and chemotherapy sessions. Also, as time went on, she worked diligently and discovered food I could and would eat, kept my precious birds fed so I could watch them from my chair, and did all the chores associated with the house and yard. She was an incredible caretaker.

Talking to Cancer

I know you are living in my lung. And the longer you live in me, the bigger you will get. I know you will try to live in other parts of my body as well. And I know that ultimately, we both can't live in my body at the same time. One of us must die for the other one to live.

I have been afraid of you since I was a child, but I need for you to understand something that is very important. Now that *you* are here, now that *you* are real, now that *you* are out of your darkness and have invaded my light, I won't be afraid of *you* anymore. I need for you to know and believe that. I also won't be angry with you. I won't hate you. I won't hold any animosity toward you. I won't wonder "Why me?" I won't be depressed. And I won't allow my spirit and my light to disintegrate in your dark presence.

I have thought long and hard about this upcoming journey, and I know I will want and need my God, my family, my friends and the thoughts and prayers of people I do not even know. I will welcome an abundance of positive energy and belief in the divine, the earth, the universe, and humanity's inexplicable ability to powerfully connect to one another. I will embrace it all as it fills my being with profound wonder and power.

And because I believe this will happen, I will be brave. I will be strong. I will be patient. I will be at peace. I will be unafraid. I will be confident in the strength and prayers and energy of others to help me conquer this life challenge. This is the path I will create. I will place my trust and faith not only in my God and others but also in the professionals who will treat and support me.

This will not be a war. I will not use my energy and my power to fight you or the negativity which you depend on to thrive. Instead, I will surround myself with prayer, white healing light, and positive energy. I will play a huge part in my own healing.

You may stay for a while. I will accept this as my fate. But make no mistake. Ultimately you will leave my body. You must accept this as your fate as well. I will be whole and strong again. You are not my journey. This is *my* journey, and I will thrive.

All proceeds from the sale of this book will be donated to cancer research.

ALIEN

I'm sitting next to my friend, Carol H. My wife, Peg, is in Austin packing for our permanent move to Rehoboth Beach, and Carol was kind enough to agree to accompany me on this dreaded but necessary appointment. Of all my friends, I knew Carol would be calmest, most supportive, and take clear and concise notes if needed. We are watching Dr. K turn on the huge machine that fills most of the exam room. He tells us that the low-dose CT scan will show multiple very thin slices of the bones, blood vessels, and tissues inside of my chest, and that the scan will also show the two abnormalities that are of concern and that we will discuss.

As the machine starts whirring, he shows the first slice that begins with my shoulders. And at every slice after that, he explains exactly where we are on my body and what we are looking at. I'm wondering how long it will take him to reach my lungs. I'm getting more nervous and impatient as every slice gets nearer to the abnormalities. I feel like we are on a family road trip and he's needlessly pointing out everything of interest he sees along the way.

None of it makes any sense to me, and it's very difficult to wrap my head around the fact that each of these slices is a part of my body. The mental image of pre-packaged slices of deli meat flashes in my mind. I'm trying to pay attention,

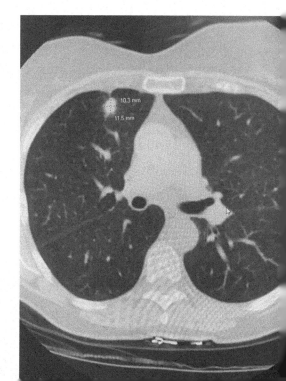

but my mind wants to wander. It doesn't matter where—maybe to the sights and smells of a walk on the beach, or sitting in my favorite chair with my Bose headphones listening to Vivaldi's Four Seasons, or imagining the thrill I get cycling on the trails in Cape Henlopen State Park. The nearer we get to the "abnormalities," the more I want to escape and be anywhere but here.

Finally, after what feels like hours, he points to what looks like an alien, the image of the ugly and repugnant creature living in my chest. I stare at it and am sure my body has been invaded by a superior and fearless creature from another planet. It resembles a large, sleeping tarantula with an off-centered, black, roundish body, and spindly legs. Each leg differs in length and thickness, and I wonder how it walks with all of its imperfections. There seem to be no eyes or mouth. How does it see and eat, I wonder? Its hideous appearance reminds me of the ghoulish beast that I imagined hid under my bed when I was a child. I can feel the ferocity and power of this alien.

Dr. K points to the abnormal lymph node in the middle of my chest. It's very big and round, and its huge size makes it seem very ominous. I'm sure it's the alien's space ship. The perimeter is covered with a distinctive dull haze, and I think it must be the exterior lighting system the alien uses when travelling to places other than my body.

I stare at the alien and its spaceship, and I know I am in deep trouble. I'm certain that one of us must die for the other to live. It takes all my self-control to not rip my chest open and try to kill it with my bare hands. I want the alien and his ship gone. I want them gone now.

Balance

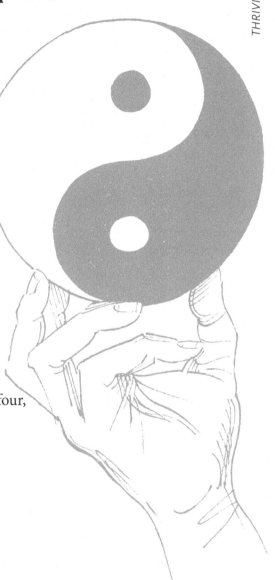

I stand on one foot, cupping
the other foot in my hand,
instep to palm, and reach
the free hand forward,
like one of Degas's dancers
poised on the dusty floor
of the practice studio.
They held the pose
far longer than I will, far
straighter than I can,
with far more grace, long
enough for the artist
to capture them in pastel.
I make it through three breaths, four,
maybe five, before
my ankle wobbles and I step
back on to the carpet
of the yoga studio
where noon sun trickles
its caramel light
into the windows.

A few seconds may be all
we can hope for
in seeking balance,
and maybe it is enough.

Maybe, standing unsure

in the real places,

like the hospital waiting room

or the steps to the plane,

or the edge of the storm-swollen stream,

all we can hope for

is the memory

of those few breaths

when one leg

holds us

to the earth.

Ellen Collins

Blood Sisters

Barbie introduced herself as I settled into the chair in the phlebotomy room. I told her I was starting to feel like a human pin cushion.

Barbie laughed as she moved the syringe nearer to my vein. "I have two kids to feed, and the more blood Dr. M needs, the more chance I have of making enough money to feed them. You wouldn't want my kids to starve, would you?"

I knew from the beginning that I would like her. She had a great sense of humor, and if I insulted her in a joking way, she always would do me one better. And any time there was another patient in the room, I would groan like she was killing me.

"Geez, Barbie," I would moan. "You've missed my vein three times. Am I your first patient or are you hung over? Your hands are shaking like crazy!"

She would retort, "Sorry, I'm a little nervous. I was supposed to receive my mail-order license last week. Thank God these mistakes don't count against me yet."

One day when I was in the infusion room getting my scheduled chemo, I looked up and there stood Barbie.

"Can I sit a minute?" She took a deep breath and said, "I had breast cancer a few years back. It was incredibly scary. Everything was new and there were so many people and procedures that sometimes I didn't know what to do or which way to turn. The hardest part was finding someone outside of my family to talk to—someone who already had cancer and understood how hard it was for me." I was stunned. Here was my insult-and-joke-around-with buddy not only being very serious, but sharing that she also had cancer and it was scary for her, too.

Barbie smiled and told me that if I needed or wanted to, I could always talk to her. We chatted for a while, and then she looked at her watch and quickly stood. She handed me a card with her work and cell numbers, and told me that she needed to leave because she only had a half hour lunch.

"You gave up your lunch time to talk to me?"

She gave me a huge grin. "This was far more important than a tuna sandwich." She patted me on the hand, and off she went.

Although my bloodwork is now done through my port, I still stop in the phlebotomy room to see Barbie every time I have to go to Tunnell Cancer Center. We are also friends on Facebook, and we chit-chat on occasion. Barbie was a huge ray of sunshine during my cancer, and will always hold a very special place in my heart.

Barbie

Brave-NOT

I was cycling in my neighborhood when I saw my close friends Judith and Robin in their driveway. Robin was also my thoracic surgeon's Physician Assistant and had assisted Dr. W in the operating room for my lung surgery.

I chit-chatted with Judith for a few minutes about friend and neighbor topics, and when we came up a moment for air, Robin said, "I've been thinking a lot about you and my sister these past few days. You remind me so much of each other." Robin's sister had died of acute myeloid leukemia a few months back. I stayed silent and waited for her to explain. "I've been in this business for over twenty years, and both of your attitudes still amaze me. Not once did I ever hear either of you complain about having cancer or say, 'why me?' or get angry or feel sorry for yourself or even think of giving up. You were always positive and calm and hopeful. You are both the bravest women I have ever known."

I stood staring at Robin in disbelief. I had not been brave at all. I did possess bravery, but it did not emanate from my being nor did I deserve any credit for its presence.

When I first discovered I had lung cancer, I was a total mental and emotional mess. I was frightened and anxious and horrified, and I couldn't even concentrate on how to make a decent cup of coffee. I walked around in a total daze, numb and directionless, with no purpose or reason for anything I did or any place I went.

I walked the beach for endless hours, trying to find "me," searching for that Type A woman who could conquer the world, who moved halfway across the country to take a straight commission job with only one hundred dollars in the bank, who never backed down, who always found a solution to every problem, who was afraid of nothing or no one. Where did that "me" go? How could I lose all of that because I had cancer?

I prayed a lot on those walks—to God, to St. Michael, to the Universe, to my Higher Power, to the eternal energy that connects us all. And on one of those walks, a light exploded in my soul, and I suddenly realized that this was all part of a bigger and greater plan. I had a choice to make. I could fight cancer with anger and rage, treat it as my mortal enemy, and use all of my arrogant, negative energy to try to destroy it. I could run from cancer and curl up in an emotional ball and share myself with no one, become bitter and angry and alone, in fear and loneliness. Or I could choose the only option left—I could be vulnerable and reach out to others for love and prayers and support, and fill my being with their light, their strength, their energy and their sustenance. I could simply be courageous enough to let go of my Type A arrogant self and trust others with my very essence, as I had never done before. I thought long and hard about these choices. And down deep, I knew I only had one choice that would give me the chance to not only live but to become a better person.

Whatever appeared as "bravery" to my friend Robin, was simply the miracle of receiving love and peace. The only thing I actually did was open my being to so many giving and caring and generous and kind people, many of whom I have yet to meet in person. I reached out and touched others, asked for their prayers, told them my true and deep feelings, even when I was

Robin

feeling alone or frightened or depressed. By being sincerely vulnerable, I received their loving words and actions that filled me with deep and lasting inner peace, positivity, and a calm that I had never experienced. It truly changed the core of my being. All I had to do was open my heart and soul and accept their precious and treasured gifts.

THEY were the brave ones. THEY were the ones who gave themselves to me with no strings attached, not expecting a single thing in return. It was THEIR love, THEIR energy, THEIR peace, THEIR calm, and THEIR strength that lived within me. I was simply blessed enough to be the recipient of all of their miracles of love, and to live these gifts that they so generously gave me.

This experience was life-altering, and these changes remain within me. If I could go back in time and have the choice of staying who I was before cancer and never getting cancer, or experience my cancer journey and keep all of the lessons and miracles I received during that journey, there is absolutely no doubt in my mind or heart that I would choose the cancer journey and who I am today. I deeply believe it was all part of the greater plan.

Breathing (Pulmonary Function) Test

- A non-invasive test that measures how well the lungs are working
- Measures lung volume, capacity, rate of flow, and gas exchange
- Used to check lung function before surgery or other procedures in patients who have lung or heart issues, who are smokers, or who have other health conditions
- Assesses treatment for asthma, emphysema, and other chronic lung problems

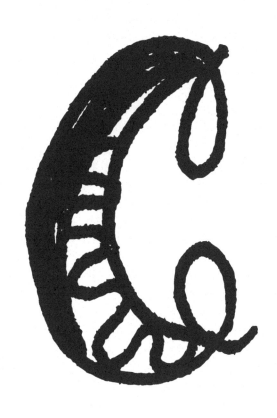

Cards

My mother was an absolute greeting card freak. You could forget to call her on her birthday, an anniversary, or a holiday, but if you didn't get her a card, or the card you did send didn't arrive until after the appropriate day, you were definitely on the doo-doo list. She also loved her cards to be big and beautiful. That, of course, meant they had to be Hallmark, and at a minimum, 6 by 8 inches. That little extra perk always resulted in her cooking your favorite meal when you visited. And if you really wanted to be the favorite of five children, you had to be sure the card arrived at least a week before the event. She always placed her cards on top of the television, and yours would end up in front of everyone else's if it arrived first. To make it even sweeter, it normally would stay there at least two weeks after the occasion.

I never understood my mother's obsession with cards and why they, over any other act or show of affection, were so important to her. I never understood, that is, until I had cancer. Cancer isn't like a cold that lasts two weeks or a kidney stone that passes and you are well. It's a long ride with many twists and turns and ups and downs. And no matter how brave or positive you remain, the "touch" of another—either physically or in words—makes it so much easier and more tolerable.

I was so very blessed with cards. I couldn't wait to go to the mailbox. Some days there were as many as five or six cards. Some days there were fewer, but there was almost always at least one. I received cards from friends, family, my fellow church members, members of my various clubs, and yes, my 1967 high school graduating class. I also received them from many people I didn't know. Several people added me to their church prayer list, and many of those people sent cards and notes of encouragement. I even had friends who were so thoughtful they sent me three or four cards over time, realizing that once the initial group of cards hit, I might not receive any more.

I did very well handling my chemo, and for the first, second and fourth infusions, I was able to function well. The third infusion was my greatest challenge and there were a few days that were very, very tough. It was on my worst day ever that a thick manila envelope arrived in the mail. I wasn't up to opening it, but Peg encouraged me and said that it might make me feel better. Here's what I found:

5-29-19

Hello Kim,

My name is Gail and I met your friend. I'll leave it up to you to figure out who it is. :). Anyway, we were talking at a casino and then suddenly your friend became very serious and told me your story. When she asked me to pray for you, I said certainly, no problem, consider it done. What she didn't know was that I am a theology teacher at a Catholic school. So, I told her that I would add you to our prayer chain at school. Then I would have the freshmen and sophomores make you some cards. We are thinking and praying for you. Enjoy reading your cards.

Gail

Inside the envelope were 83 handmade cards. All were made from a piece of white 8 1/2 x 11 copy paper folded in half. Each student created their own cover design and their own message, and each of their personalities shone through as bright as the sun. It is impossible to put into words the effect this treasure had on my spirit and even my body.

It touched me so deeply that even writing this today, I cannot help but cry and feel deep love and gratitude to the children who gave me their hearts and prayers.

I still have every single card that was mailed or given to me. And sometimes on a rainy day or during this pandemic, I randomly take a few out and fill my heart and spirit with the warmth and love I was so very privileged to receive. Cards, I now realize, have far more meaning than I ever imagined.

I hope my mother in heaven knows I've changed my mind.

Chemo Brain

Almost everyone I know has either heard of or knows someone who has chemo brain. It's a common term used by cancer survivors to describe thinking and memory problems. Chemo brain can occur during and after cancer treatment. The reasons aren't well understood, and many experts think there may be multiple causes. No matter what the causes, chemo brain can be a frustrating and debilitating side effect of cancer and its treatment. Below are the most common traits of chemo brain.

- Short-term memory issues
- Taking longer than usual to complete routine tasks
- Trouble with verbal memory, such as remembering a conversation
- Trouble with visual memory, such as recalling an image or list of words
- Difficulty concentrating
- Difficulty finding the right word
- Difficulty learning new skills
- Difficulty multi-tasking
- Feeling of mental grogginess
- Short attention span
- Difficulty processing

During the pandemic, Peg and I have played gin rummy several times a week. As simple as the game is, I experience the same things every time we play—trying to remember who dealt last, having to ask for the score after every round, getting confused when I must choose an option such as saving three of a kind or using one of the three cards to make a run.

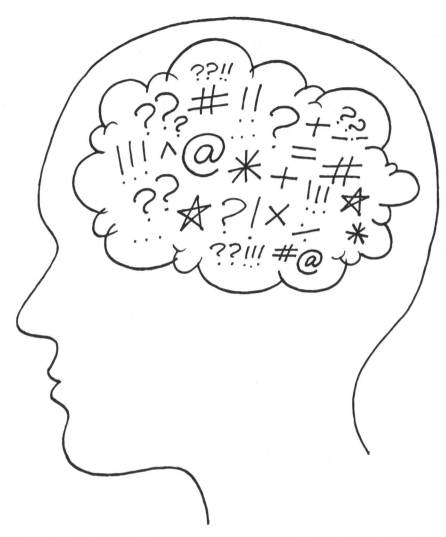

If I talk with a neighbor on my morning walk with my dog Jake or see a friend at the grocery store, when I start to tell Peg about it, I find myself confused in the middle of the story. And if the friend has asked me to pass a message on to Peg, I either forget the message or only remember half of it.

I ask Peg the same question over and over.

I often struggle with finding the word I want to say and sometimes just give up the conversation. An ironic example is my recent attempt to tell Peg about a friend who was diagnosed with dementia. No matter how hard I tried, I couldn't remember the word, and I ended up saying, "What's that word that describes someone who loses their memory and gets confused about places and things?"

Prior to chemo, I could write, read, or play one of my musical instruments for hours. Now I get mentally tired after an hour.

I can no longer focus on more than one thing at a time. If I'm baking cookies, I can't focus on the laundry when the cookies are in the oven. And I have to write down the time I put the cookies in and the time I need to take them out. Otherwise, I forget. And no, setting the timer doesn't work. It is too confusing.

Some of the chemo brain symptoms have lessened over time, while others remain constant. I am blessed with having a very patient wife who understands that I truly am trying to pay attention. There are times, though, when interacting with the rest of the world is annoying for others and embarrassing and frustrating for me.

Colossal Compassion

We are in the Tunnell Cancer Center lobby waiting to be called for my fourth and final chemotherapy infusion. My heart is beating so loud I can hear it in my ears. I am so anxious that I can hardly put two words together. Rather than sitting with Peg, I am pacing around the crowded waiting room, trying to work off the tension and negative energy that's exploding in my body.

There is a strict protocol for each person's chemotherapy regimen. Mine is to receive 4 infusions, 21 days apart. Ten or eleven days between each treatment, I return for a full blood work-up to assess my white count, platelet count, and functions of my major organs. I wait in the lobby while the tests are completed, and I am then called to meet with Dr. M who will determine if all 36 categories are in a range for me to continue chemotherapy.

My first and second interim labs were off the charts, and I passed all categories with flying colors. I expected the labs after the third infusion to be the same and was waiting to hear the good news. But when Dr. M entered the room, she was not smiling, and I knew something was wrong. She told me that both my white blood count and three other categories were not in range.

I looked at Dr. M. "But they have to be in range. I have to get my infusion on the 21st day or the chemo won't kill the cancer. I know it won't. I just know it won't." I started to hyperventilate and feel dizzy.

Tracy

She said, "Your fourth infusion is scheduled a week from today. Why don't you come in twenty minutes early and we'll redo your lab work? Maybe it will improve by then."

So here I stand in the lobby of the Tunnell Cancer Center on the originally scheduled day for my last chemo infusion. They finally call my name and lead me into the infusion room. I see Tracy, my scheduled nurse for the day, and tell her I have to go to the blood draw room first and get lab work done because I didn't pass the tests to get chemo.

"Hold on, Cowgirl, and calm down," she says. "You're on my watch today, and I can draw blood right from your chest port. There's no need to get stuck with a needle. Come on, let's get you set up."

I'm a mess. "But what if my labs aren't good enough? What am I going to do? How will I finish my chemo? I have to finish right on time so the cancer is killed."

Tracy puts a hand on each of my shoulders and looks intently into my eyes. "Your labs will be fine. You're going to get your fourth and final treatment TODAY." Between her firm but soothing touch and

the intensity of her eyes, I find myself calming a bit. She draws one vial of blood, places it in the lab basket, and turns to leave.

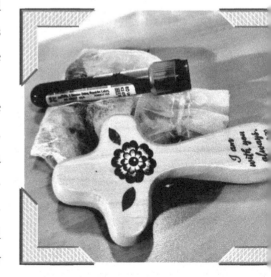

"Wait, Tracy!" I take the little wooden cross out of my pocket. "My sister sent this to me in a chemotherapy bag full of goodies. I take it to every test, appointment, and chemo infusion. Could you place it in the basket with my blood?"

Her eyes moisten, and she smiles slightly. "I'll do you one better," she says. She reaches in her pocket and pulls out a little bag of crystals. "I keep these with me at all times for positive energy. Let's send these, too." I give her a huge smile.

Fifteen minutes later, Tracy pulls up my lab report and winks at me. "Time to start your fourth and final infusion. Right as scheduled, by the way."

Sometimes it takes a little outside help to get through the tough times.

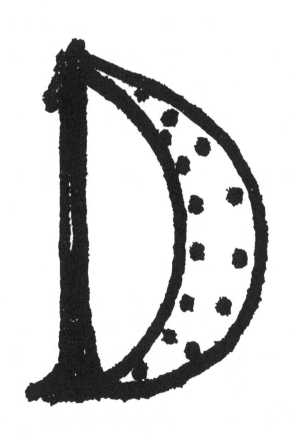

Damned

The funny part about cancer and getting all the required scans is that you're damned if you do and damned if you don't.

Gone untreated, there is no doubt that cancer will kill you. But to detect the cancer, diagnose the cancer, monitor the cancer, and follow up once the cancer is in remission, you must have a myriad of scans. And not only does each scan emit radiation, but the more scans you have, the more radiation builds up in your body.

High doses of radiation can cause cancer. BUT—since I already knew I had cancer and that cancer could cause more cancer, following the protocols and doing exactly what my doctors advised was the path I chose to follow.

Dog Days

When I met first Peg, Higgins was six years old. He was a West Highland terrier and typical for his breed—stubborn, independent, a barker, and a runner if let off-leash. He liked to chase squirrels, birds, rabbits, cats, mice, snakes—just about anything that moved. He was also incredibly handsome. His fur was snow white and soft to the touch, and he had big brown doe eyes.

Peg and Higgins had lived together all of Higgins's life, and they were fast friends and much in love with each other. So, I was the new kid on the block. He was not aggressive or nasty to me, but he never selected me when he had the option of doing something with Peg. He liked me, but he was 100% a Mama's boy.

That all changed the day I came home from the hospital after my lobectomy. I was in pretty rough shape and needed Peg's help to do just about everything. Although Higgins wasn't any help in that department, from that day to almost six months later when I finished chemotherapy, he never left my side. If I took a three-hour afternoon nap, he was snuggled next to me or on my pillow nose to nose. If I used my walker and took a very slow stroll in the neighborhood with Peg, Higgins kept pace and never once tried to run ahead or chase one of the neighborhood critters. If I was watching television or reading a book, he instinctively knew he couldn't sit in my lap or push into the right side of my body. But he made sure he was in the chair with me or at my feet if the chair was too small. And although he was a go-to-bed-late and get-up-late kind of guy just like his mother, he would go to bed early and wake up early with me.

It's hard to explain what comfort and joy this furry little fellow brought me. He was always there, my little bodyguard and loving care-taker. He gave up fast walks, chasing vermin, and his normal sleep patterns for me. He did whatever I did, whether he liked it or not. And he never asked for a single thing in return. It may sound a bit odd, but I learned many lessons about giving and caring from Higgins, and every chance I get, I will pass them on.

Higgins

Each Leaf

letting go of its branch
takes a brave chance
that the air will cushion

its fall through autumn's
bronze light, sun still
in its veined heart.

It knows only
where it has been,
not leafspill, leafdrop,

not the milky sky at its back,
the world spun upside down,
and it must call forth

vast reservoirs of faith
to finally release
and trust

its solitary flight
and its far, uncertain landing.

Ellen Collins

Einstein Can't be Wrong

Receiving the diagnosis of lung cancer, followed by a major operation and chemotherapy, was a frightening and mind-numbing experience. In the early stages, emotions came in waves. Physical strength was mediocre at best. Spiritual fortitude wavered and often got lost in darkness. Each day brought its own set of physical, emotional, spiritual, and psychological needs. Many times, I was so mired in the challenge and fears of the day, I couldn't even label what it was I really needed to feel better.

But I innately knew right from the beginning that if I could find a way to be brave enough to reach out to others for support, my experience would be far easier and more healing than attempting to go on this journey by myself. I also realized that no single person could help with all of the nuts and bolts that I needed to stay positive and serene each day. Most important, I knew I needed others because to be alone would be incredibly difficult. I gain my energy and strength externally from others, and for me, that was a must to be successful in what I knew would be a frightening voyage.

It didn't take me long to recognize that my most important need was the state of my spirituality. The least important was my physical level of comfort or discomfort. The more I was able to fulfill my spiritual needs, the less physical pain and discomfort I would feel.

So many people told me that the key to winning the battle was to stay positive throughout the experience. I thought that was a nice thing to say from family and friends, but I didn't give it much credibility in the reality of the seriousness and statistics associated with my diagnosis. But when I heard the same thing over and over from the medical staff, both nurses and doctors, the more I began to believe it. They shared many stories and actual miracles they observed. And it was obvious from their expressions, tones, and words that they deeply believed that there can be far more at work than medicine in the healing process of a serious medical situation.

One last event that gave me the final push to have the intention and commitment to a journey of positivity and fortitude happened in, of all places, a dentist's office. It was just after I had learned I would need an operation, and I was leafing through a magazine. A quote caught my eye.

"There are only two ways to live your life.
One is as though nothing is a miracle.
The other is as though everything is a miracle."
Albert Einstein

At that moment, I decided if it was good enough for Einstein, it was good enough for me.

Everlasting Faith

I love everything about Maya Angelou, and most of all, her poetry. There was one quote in particular that helped me when I was feeling low emotionally or spiritually. "Let gratitude be the pillow upon which you kneel to say your nightly prayer. And let faith be the bridge you build to overcome evil and welcome good."

I realized very early, if my journey was to be successful, that faith—a firm belief and trust where there was no proof—must be my fundamental bedrock. Faith in my doctors, faith that my diagnosis would be something I could accept, faith in a successful lung surgery, faith in the Beebe hospital system where I would receive treatment, faith that my body could withstand the very harsh chemotherapy, faith that the chemotherapy would work. And most of all, faith in God. I knew I would need deep and abiding faith to believe that this journey was an essential part of my life, no matter what its outcome.

Although I was raised Catholic and attended Catholic schools, I later moved away from Catholicism but remained very spiritual. My belief in God, prayer, angels, and miracles still existed. And when times were tough, this was the foundation of my ability to endure and rise above adversity. I prayed to God, and especially to St. Michael and St. Raphael. I reached out to friends, family, and medical personnel to pray for me, and many placed me on their church's prayer lists as well. I also had other friends who sent positive energy, mental good wishes, and some who crossed their fingers for me. I even had two dear friends who performed daily remote Reiki which I openly accepted. I believed and continue to believe that the power and energy of many hearts and minds focused on good and the same goal can create miracles.

When I was first diagnosed, my faith was badly shaken. I was in shock. I was numb. I was frightened. And it seemed everything I heard, every place I went, everything I saw, all I encountered was lung cancer. There were horrific and frightening ads on television and radio, people next to me in restaurants talking about their relatives or co-workers with lung cancer who died in pain, and friends sharing stories about someone they knew wasting away from the disease. Everywhere I turned, lung cancer was there, seeping into the very fabric of my being.

One night I felt particularly alone and anxious. The day had been packed with lung cancer reminders, and I was depressed and filled with dread. I decided to attend a Rehoboth Beach Writers Guild poetry evening. Local folks were reading their work at a popular restaurant. I very much enjoyed the first two readings. And then a shy young woman walked up to the podium. She was visibly very nervous and apprehensive. As she stood in front of the mike, she cleared her throat, looked out at the audience and said, "I wrote this poem about the strongest and bravest man I've ever known—my father. He struggled and fought valiantly, never losing hope. For almost two years, he struggled and struggled, and finally three weeks ago he lost his battle to lung cancer."

I audibly gasped, and as I stood up, my chair clattered behind me. I ran out of the restaurant to my car, and sat inside crying and shaking. I couldn't stand another minute. I felt lost and empty, filled with fear and despair. I'm not sure what evil really is, but I did and do believe it exists. I sensed it as a darkness that was getting closer and closer to invading me. At one moment, it took the shape of a fleeting shadow that I saw out of the corner of my eye. In the next moment, it felt like a heavy fog following me, waiting to suffocate me. I could almost hear its voice and see its face, and I knew I was starting to lose myself to evil. Lung cancer was everywhere and evil was coming to get me. I would suffer and die because evil was stronger and more powerful than I could ever be.

I drove as fast as I dared, and when I opened my front door, I instantly knew evil was there. The air felt heavy and filled with doom. When I looked up at the open doorway of my bedroom on the second-floor landing, I knew that it was in my bedroom, waiting for me. It had now penetrated my home and I was sure that only one of us would remain at the end of this night.

This was a "do or die" moment for me. I could go into a fetal position and live in anger, fear and depression, or I could face the evil and try to destroy it. In an instant, I made my choice. I started screaming at the top of my lungs. I screamed every curse word I could think of at this faceless, bodiless entity who had come to destroy my faith in God, myself, and my life. I screamed that I was stronger than it. I screamed that God and Light and Faith were my choices. And I screamed for it to get out of my body, out of my home, and out of my world. I screamed over and over and over again until I had no voice left. I was NOT those lung cancer ads. I was NOT those horrific lung cancer stories. I was NOT my friend's sister or anyone else with lung cancer. I was ME. And it was MY journey, and I CHOSE to take it with faith in God and good. And when I could scream no more, I felt the air swoosh, and I could breathe again. The house was once more my warm and welcoming bungalow. I looked up at my bedroom, and knew it was only my bedroom.

Evil left me that night and never returned. From that night on, people sensed the difference in me. I was filled with deep feelings of peace, serenity, and positivity. Throughout my journey these feelings rarely left me, and when they did, I would pray for their presence, and they always would return quickly and fully. I was able to reach out to others when I felt weak or ill. And because I chose to be open and vulnerable instead of fearful and angry, I was surrounded with love, support, positive energy, and light. As crazy as it sounds, my cancer experience was a period of time filled with holiness, peace and serenity. I felt one with my God, the love and support of family and friends, and the miraculous care I received from the Beebe staff.

Faith—a power and goodness far greater than myself—guided me through my cancer. It helped me transcend my own human frailties and fears. My spirit remained whole, my mind stayed strong, and my heart was filled with light and love. As I think back on that period of my life, I can say in all truth, that if I could have chosen NOT to have cancer and to remain the arrogant and angry woman I had become, or I could HAVE cancer and experience the wonderful transformation I was so blessed to receive, I would choose the cancer.

Sometimes we just don't know what truly is best for us until we have a little faith.

Everything

I never thought I'd live in a beach town. I haven't been to many beach towns, but those I've visited are honky-tonk. Some have a boardwalk. Some don't. But they all share the same smells and atmosphere. Old, used up grease for the French fries, cotton candy and candy apple machines, the big fat hot dogs in the little buns, and always boxes of salt water taffy in all colors and flavors. There are the tourist stores with their T-shirts so thin you can almost see through them, the plastic beach toys, and inner tubes with mermaids for the girls and whales for the boys. And, of course, the beach towels, flippers, and masks for the teenagers.

Rehoboth Beach looks, smells and feels different than any other beach town I've visited. The boardwalk is clean, wide, and very well maintained. It's a little over a mile long, and a great place to walk or sit on one of the wooden benches and people-watch or listen to the ocean waves. The side streets have quaint, unique shops filled with the wares of local artists and craftspeople. Small cafés and restaurants are sprinkled among the shops. The clean, narrow walkways remind me of picturesque alleys in the small towns of Europe. A large open gazebo is positioned right before the boardwalk. It houses summer and winter band concerts, community meetings, and holiday celebrations. People come from all over the area to enjoy and participate in the myriad of festivities.

In 2013, Peg and I visited Rehoboth Beach for a week. We were getting married in a near-by town, and we fell in love with the area. On October 6, we took our wedding vows and purchased an adorable little saltbox-style home. We started traveling to Rehoboth Beach every summer. Each year we stayed longer and longer, and in our fifth year, we decided to sell the Austin property, rent the little saltbox, and buy a larger home in the Rehoboth Beach area and live here permanently. The decision was an easy one, and I have never regretted it.

In the spring, summer, and fall, I love walking the beach, photography, golfing, cycling on the roads and incredible trails in the parks, weekly card parties, local theatre, the Women and Jazz festivals, and meeting friends for happy hours, regular dinners, and birthday celebrations. Peg also loves many of those same activities, as well as tanning at the beach, swimming in the ocean, and fishing with friends.

Unlike most beach towns, Rehoboth Beach also thrives in the wintertime. It is a town of diversity and activities. There is something for everyone—the Rehoboth Beach Writing Guild, the Sussex Cycling Group, Coastal Camera Club, local theatre, two choral groups, hiking events, musical groups, charity events, and both the library and Browseabout Books continually offer programs for all ages. If it sounds a bit like heaven, it is.

In the middle of December 2018, Peg returned to Austin to pack our belongings and sell our home. We knew this would take several weeks or even months to complete, so I stayed in Rehoboth Beach at our bungalow for the rest of the winter, packing what could be packed and coordinating workmen for repairs and various things we needed done for the new house.

At the end of March 2019, Peg was still in Austin, and after a standard check-up, I was told that my low-dose thoracic CT scan was abnormal. I thought about returning to Austin and having my medical care there, knowing that if this was serious, MD Anderson in Houston was a two-hour drive or a 30-minute plane ride away. And my wife was there and must remain there for at least the next several weeks. But we also had an incredible group of friends in Rehoboth that functioned more like a tight-knit and loving family. In short, Rehoboth Beach had everything we ever wanted.

Sometimes we must make decisions of the heart versus decisions of the head. Some deep voice within me kept repeating the same phrase over and over again. "Stay. You are home. You have everything you've ever really wanted right here." And stay I did. It was one of the best decisions of my life. I had a long and arduous journey ahead, and I was exactly where I needed to be—home on every level. I still smile just thinking about it.

Fabulous Friday

My first PET scan took place on Friday, April 12, 2019. I was finished a little after 3:00 p.m. The nuclear technician told me the results might be ready Monday, or Tuesday at the latest. I knew it was going to be a very, very long weekend.

But as I was headed out of my house less than three hours later, my cell phone rang. It was Dr. K. I was sure this was NOT a good sign.

"I have the results of the PET scan," he said. "I have some good news and some bad news. Which would you like first?" I asked for the bad news. "We must aggressively go after your tumor. I have already set you up with an appointment with a thoracic surgeon."

"And the good news?" I asked.

"The PET scan showed no other lesions in your body. It was clean."

I felt the weight of the world lift off my shoulders. I could live with the tumor being malignant. I could live with an operation. But all my prayers had been answered. The cancer hadn't spread. I was jumping up and down, laughing, crying, thanking God, thanking Dr. K, and thanking the universe in general. I took a breath and then asked him why he was calling so soon after the test. Why wasn't he playing nine holes of twilight golf or having a beer with some of his friends?

Dr. K and me

Dr. K told me that he knew the test results were a big worry for me, and he didn't want me wondering and worrying all weekend and into the next week. "I wouldn't want that for my family," he said, "and I didn't want that for you."

One can't buy this type of caring and dedication with a paycheck. Perhaps in the scheme of the world, this wasn't a major deal. But Dr. K saved me hours and days of unnecessary anxiety and fear, and I will be forever grateful to him for giving up the start of his weekend to make the start of mine a happy and relieved time.

Favorite Saying

One day you'll wake up and look in the mirror, and life as you know it will be over. All you have is today. Don't waste a precious moment of it.

I've believed this since high school. I've thought about it every day, and through the years I have said it hundreds of times to others.

And one day I woke up, looked in the mirror, and I had lung cancer.

One day you'll wake up and look in the mirror, and life as you know it will be over. All you have is today. Don't waste a precious moment of it.

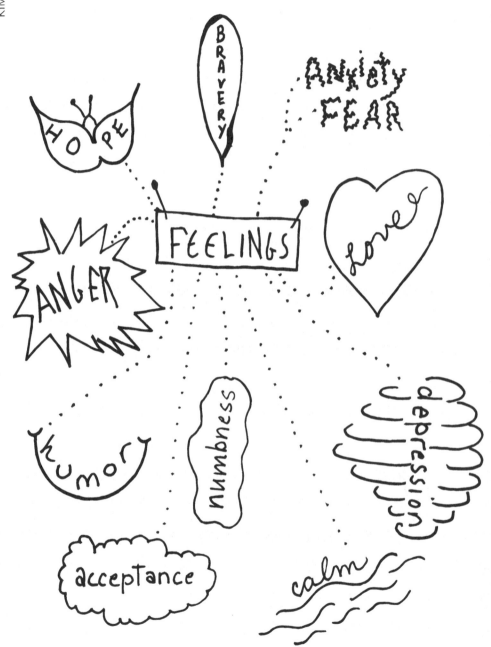

Forgiveness

Forgiving myself was one of the toughest things for me to do during my cancer experience. Sometimes I would get really frightened or impatient or worn out or just plain feel sorry for myself. The worst times were when I would imagine horrible outcomes for an upcoming test, procedure, or chemotherapy infusion. Invariably, the event was never as scary or as painful as I had imagined. I had wasted lots of energy on something that never occurred. When I'd look back and think about all the emotions and fears I had put myself through, I felt angry and disappointed in myself.

Even though I was blessed that these emotional occurrences were few and far between, it still took me a while to simply admit that I was human, and that it was ok to be weak or afraid now and then. I thought I should be stronger or better or more in control. After a while, I realized that none of us can be those things all the time, and it was enough just to try to do the best that I could at the time. As trite as that sounds, it gave me great comfort and the ability to forgive myself when needed.

LOVE IS AN ACT OF ENDLESS FORGIVENESS

*uck Cancer

When my inner and outer circle of friends learned I had lung cancer, people started to drop by. Most would bring a gift. I also received gifts in the mail from relatives and friends. I would have loved things like Word Search, crossword books, games, jigsaw puzzles, mystery novels, and even one of those adult coloring books with a set of colored pencils. Between the operation and chemotherapy, I had a lot of free time on my hands.

Interestingly enough, I didn't get a single one of those things. Here is a sampling of my gifts:

- 3 *uck cancer mugs—a hot pink, gray marble, and a navy blue
- 2 *uck cancer appointment books—one paisley and the other forest green. Both had sections for tests, chemo, doctor appointments, times for medicines, etc.
- 2 *uck cancer pairs of socks—both cotton—one white with black letters, the other red with white letters
- 8 *uck cancer cards
- 2 *uck cancer bracelets—one Morse code, and the other copper
- 2 *uck cancer journals—one striped and thin lined, the second teal and college lined
- 3 * uck cancer T-shirts—a bright blue with white letters, a yellow with black letters, and a charcoal gray with black letters
- 1 *uck cancer tote bag—bright orange with white letters
- 1 *uck cancer dog bandana—black with white letters

As these gifts came in, I would thank each individual and place the gift in an empty bureau drawer. I didn't want to *uck cancer. I simply wanted it to go away, and while the cancer was in my body, I wanted it to allow the chemotherapy to do its job.

I was thankful that I had so many kind and generous relatives and friends. But I often wondered why so many of them took the *uck cancer route versus some of the more uplifting ways to face and conquer cancer. I would have loved to wear a t-shirt that said "Cancer Warrior" or a bracelet with the message, "You've got this," or even a baseball cap that sported the words "I will beat cancer." It seemed for a heavy-duty cancer, however, they wanted a heavy-duty message. And I did appreciate that.

After I completed chemotherapy and started to get my strength back, I knew I would never use any of the *uck cancer gifts. So, I stuffed all of them but one in the *uck cancer orange tote bag and brought them to the AmVets. I later wondered if they elected to display and sell them. It would have been nice if they made a little money for their worthy cause.

I have no idea why, but I decided to keep the hot pink *uck cancer mug. Perhaps as a memento of a time now past.

Get a Scan

A low-dose CT scan can detect early-stage lung cancer, identifying abnormalities as small as a grain of rice. What you should know:

- It uses no dyes or injections.
- It uses 5 times less radiation than the conventional CT scan.
- It takes less time than the conventional CT scan.
- Medicare and many private health insurance plans cover the screening.

People who are current or former smokers over the age of 50 probably meet the eligibility criteria.

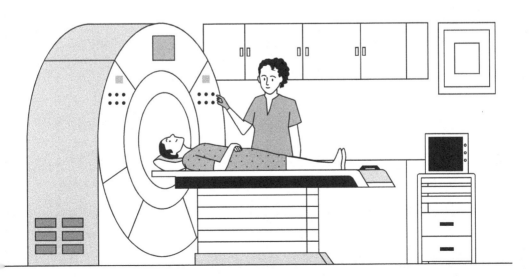

Geyser Power

Geysers are common in the United States. Yellowstone Park alone has more than five hundred. Geysers are hot springs that erupt periodically. The eruptions are the result of super-heated water below ground becoming trapped in channels that lead to the surface. As the eruption continues, the heat and pressure gradually decrease, and the eruption stops when the water reservoir is depleted or the steam runs out.

Although much of the course of my cancer was emotionally and spiritually smooth, there were times when I turned into a human geyser. In those instances, I was stripped of being brave, serene, and positive. I erupted, felt like my insides would explode, my heart would catapult out of my chest, and my brain would disintegrate and turn into powder. I was trapped without control of an outcome, and I couldn't go back to normal until my emotions were depleted or my energy was exhausted. As rarely as these eruptions occurred, it took a day or two for me to recoup from being a human geyser.

Geyser 1
Watching Dr. K pull up my low-dose CT scan and waiting for him to tell me if I had cancer

Geyser 2
Answering Dr. K's phone call to find out if the PET scan showed whether my cancer had metastasized to other parts of my body

Geyser 3
Waiting for Rudy to tell me if I passed the two-hour breathing test so I could have my lung operation to remove my cancerous tumor

Geyser 4

Waking up in the pre-recovery room after my lobectomy operation and screaming that I wanted my wife, Peg

Geyser 5

Recently waiting for the results of a PET scan to determine if the bony protrusion on my shoulder blade was cancer

I think we all become a geyser now and then. As exhausting and horrifying as that experience can be, it is part of being human. And there is nothing so sweet as when the geyser subsides, returning us to peace and serenity.

Ghost

As soon as word got around that I had lung cancer, people seemed to fall into two camps. The first camp treated me like they always had. They were comfortable and open and caring with me. They would ask how I was feeling, if they could do anything to help, and, as always, they would bust my chops on occasion. The second camp would go out of their way to avoid me. And if they had no other choice when seeing me out and about, they would talk to me in a whisper and look at me with eyes full of pity. On occasion, a person in the second camp might get brave and lean forward, place their hand on my arm, and in great pain say, "How are you feeling, dear?"

They already had me dead and gone, and were sure they were talking to a ghost.

Good Luck and Magic

I always believed that a little bit of good luck and magic shows up at one time or another in our lives.

When I got lung cancer, I found mine with a guy named Alec C. He was my oncologist's Physician Assistant. Every time Dr. M scheduled me for one of my many tests, I could always call Alec the day of the test or the next day and get the results. It was so much less stressful than waiting for my scheduled follow-up appointment with Dr. M, which was normally several days or a week away.

One very special time comes to mind. We were at the height of this new pandemic with makeshift patient rooms in the streets, thousands of daily deaths, no one allowed in hospitals or doctors' offices. It was during that time that I discovered a bony protrusion on my right shoulder. I had a tele-meeting with Dr. M, and because lung cancer most likely metastasizes in the brain or the bone, she scheduled a PET scan.

My test was early in the morning, and in mid-afternoon I left a message for Alec and asked if he would please call me when he received the results.

To get my mind on something else, Peg and I decided to go for a late afternoon walk. Our neighbors, Judith

Alec

and Robin, were doing yard work and we stopped to chat with them. They were also aware I was waiting for the results of the PET scan. My cell phone rang, and I immediately recognized the Beebe number.

I walked away to answer the phone, knowing it was Alec. Whatever the results, I wanted to hear them alone first. Alec introduced himself, said he had the PET scan results, and paused. It was probably a one or two second pause, but it felt like a year. I could feel my heart pounding. I was pacing back and forth like a mad woman. And then the magic words, "The PET scan showed no abnormalities."

I started jumping up and down and screaming "YES!!!" in the middle of the street. Then Peg, Judith, and Robin started laughing and yelling. Other neighbors were opening their doors and smiling.

The whole time I forgot that poor Alec was still on the phone. I asked him if he was still there. He laughed, and said he enjoyed hearing the celebration. I thanked him profusely for responding so soon, and told him he was my good luck and magic.

Guardian Angel

On March 18, 2019, I had my first appointment with Dr. B to establish a relationship with a local primary care physician. I was living in our Whisperwood Lane summer house. Peg was in Austin, Texas, packing our home and readying it to sell. Dr. B was with Mid-Atlantic Family Practice located in Millsboro, twenty miles from my home.

I really liked Dr. B. He was young, smart, friendly, interested, and very caring. We really "clicked" as people. As I started to leave, he asked if I had been a smoker. I told him I had been, and when he figured out I fit the criteria, he told me he was setting me up for a low-dose CT scan in the Beebe Medical system. It was free for anyone on Medicare.

It ended up saving my life, and it was also how I met Phyllis. She worked in Dr. B's office, and her job was to set up referral appointments for patients. It was Phyllis who called me with the date, time, and location for my scan. She was very warm and pleasant, and it was obvious she loved doing her job.

I had the scan nine days later, and Dr. B called me the same day. He explained that the scan showed abnormalities, and Phyllis would call

Phyllis

me with the referral to a Beebe pulmonologist. The pulmonologist would read the scan and determine next steps. When Phyllis called me, she could tell immediately that I was frightened and anxious.

"Are you okay? You sound really upset," she said.

"My wife's in Austin, and she'll be there for several more weeks," I replied. "I'm alone."

"Get a paper and pencil. I want you to write down my personal cell phone number. You can call me any time, day or night. I know you're afraid and being alone is hard. But we can talk, and that will help. I don't care if it's the middle of the night."

And that was the start of our connection. Although my original CT scan was ordered by Mid-Atlantic, over the next several months my medical care was taken over by the Beebe Medical system. But that didn't stop Phyllis from caring about me. No matter what test or procedure I had in the following weeks, Phyllis always called me before to tell me what it would entail so I wasn't as nervous. She also checked in afterward to learn how I was doing and get the results of the test or procedure. We stayed in touch even after Peg returned and I wasn't alone anymore. Then Phyllis cared for both of us.

As the days neared for my lobectomy, I asked her if she would pray for me, and she said she already had me on her church's prayer list. She had done this after we spoke the first time, and she said she would not take me off the list until I was cancer-free. We talked many times before the operation—about life, God, blessings, bravery, grace. And she called Peg as soon as the operation was over and every day thereafter until I was released from the ICU and sent home.

She was my angel during my recuperation, and my rock when the pathology report verified that the tumor was malignant and that I also had two cancerous lymph nodes and would need chemotherapy. Even during my treatments, she never stopped calling. She never stopped caring. She never stopped praying and keeping me calm and feeling loved. And over time, we exchanged family photos and stories of our lives and shared our thoughts.

I kept Dr. B as my primary care physician, and, on occasion, I would have a check-up appointment with him. Phyllis would always come out of the back office, and we would exchange big hugs while we caught up.

If anyone reading this essay wonders if Phyllis truly is my guardian angel, you "best sit down for the end of this tale," as they say in my home state of Maine. When Mid-Atlantic Family Practice joined the Beebe system, Phyllis lost her position at the old Mid-Atlantic, but Beebe offered her a position which she gladly accepted. She would continue to do referral calls for patients, except in the Beebe call center.

At the start of the pandemic, I had tried and tried to get into Dr. B's office for my first vaccine. But small offices were out of the vaccine, and the state had not allotted them any more. So, I decided to contact Beebe's call center to see if they had any other suggestions. Just as the phone started to ring, I turned to Peg and laughed. "Maybe St. Michael will give me a miracle and put Phyllis at the other end of this call, and she can get me a vaccine shot."

Peg smirked. "Good luck with that."

But it was Phyllis who answered the phone, even though there are fifteen Beebe operators and several shifts. I recognized her voice immediately. She told me not to wait for Beebe, and to call the state right away and get on their list. She also gave me the information about two other facilities I could contact. Both Peg and I emailed all three sites as soon as I got off the phone. Two days later I received a form from the VAMS CDC system and scheduled my shot for two days after that.

By the way, in the following months I called the scheduling center numerous times, and all but twice, I just "happened" to get Phyllis. She also just "happens" to call me when I'm anxious about an upcoming scan, have a family death or illness, or just because she has been on my mind, and I need a jolt of Phyllis.

Perhaps it is all coincidence. Perhaps it's just luck. Or perhaps we just need to have faith in things beyond our own comprehension. For me, I have no doubt that Phyllis is my life-long guardian angel.

Happy Trails

Lung cancer chemotherapy drugs are very harsh, and they can do quite a job of compromising the immune system. So, during the entire summer and fall of 2019, I was advised to stay away from the public and basically be homebound. That is somewhat easier said than done, especially living in a beach town. At first, I did a great job of behaving, but by the end of July, I was absolutely desperate to get out of the house. I was feeling a bit better, had some energy, and needed to see people and be convinced there was a thriving, living world outside of my own home.

I've always hated grocery shopping, but thank goodness, my wife, Peg, loves it. She strolls down each aisle like she is in a museum full of treasures. No item is too insignificant to admire and appreciate with a touch or a prolonged gaze. If there are a lot of sales, she may be gone for several hours with her bag full of coupons. When she does arrive home, she's all smiles.

Finally, the opportunity presented itself for me to step out into the wider world. Peg was going grocery shopping, and even that sounded like a delightful outing to me. So, in the car I hopped, and we headed for Harris-Teeter. Peg had never visited this grocery store, and she was convinced it was going to be a wonderful adventure. We both believed that the grocery store was one of the safest places for me to visit. People are not particularly close like in church pews or at a sporting event. They are also usually on the move. The aisles are pretty wide, especially in the fruit and vegetable sections. The frozen foods are all behind glass. And best of all, most grocery stores have hand sanitizer that you can use when you come in and leave. There was no need to call Triage at Tunnell Cancer Center to double-check. We had this one covered.

I couldn't believe it. The store was filled with people laughing and talking and filling their carts with delectable items. After looking at the walls of my house for so long, I was bombarded by color. In the produce aisles there were mounds of fresh fruits and vegetables in shades of red and orange and green. Melons, zucchini, lemons, lettuces, eight

varieties of apples. The deli section drew me like a magnet to the array of ham, turkey, salami, cheddar, and provolone. And what can I say to describe the bakery? Glistening pies, rows of donuts, breads fresh from the oven. Even the dairy section looked beautiful with its many cartons of yogurts and butters. It went on and on, and I was totally immersed in this wonderful experience. When the cart was full and Peg was ready to leave, I asked if we could please stay just a few more minutes. I had missed cruising two aisles. By the last aisle, my legs got shaky, and my breathing was a little labored. My body had had enough. And when I got home, I drifted off in a peaceful and happy sleep and took a long nap.

Three days later, I went to Tunnell for my third infusion. A lady who was there and being prepped for her first infusion was sitting in my four-seat pod. I heard the nurse chatting with her, and the word "grocery" caught my attention. It seems the lady was being told that chemotherapy compromises your immune system, and the two worse places you can go are the grocery store and the movie theatre.

All I can say is that my grocery store excursion was one of the most enjoyable and fulfilling experiences I had during my several months of cancer treatment. Sometimes a girl's gotta do what a girl's gotta do.

Highly Hazardous

I'm chit-chatting with Susan, my friend and Al-Anon sponsor. We are waiting for my first chemotherapy treatment to start. My wife, Peg, has a fishing tournament today, and since Susan is a retired nurse, I'm very grateful she is going to my treatment with me. The cancer staff had suggested that I bring someone along who could take notes for the first infusion because there will be a lot of important things to remember. Also, I was told that the first treatment is a six or seven-hour visit. We've been in the infusion room for about four hours and are set up in Pod 3. The volunteer staff served donuts at nine, snacks at eleven, and sandwiches at 1:00 p.m. I'm feeling pretty relaxed and satiated.

There are already several bags attached to the pole, and the liquids are entering my body through the port in my chest. My nurse, Megan, told me that during these first several hours I've been receiving meds to prevent side effects, such as an allergic reaction and nausea. They will continue infusing these antiemetic drugs, an antihistamine, and a steroid. One of the chemo infusions also requires a liter bag of potassium and magnesium to replace depleted electrolytes so that I will not get neuropathy. Saline is used to carry the medications and to flush between medications.

Around two o'clock, Susan is reading a magazine and I am doing a word search. And then out of the corner of my eye, I see someone moving toward us. She is dressed in a blue medical robe, a face mask, a hair cap, a visor, rubber gloves and rubber booties. When I see her piercing brown eyes, I realize that it is Megan, my nurse, and she looks like an astronaut or a deep-sea diver.

She is carrying two plastic bags, each filled with a different colored liquid. She is followed by another nurse. The other nurse pulls up the computer and Megan reads the labels on the two plastic bags to her. Then they double-check my information and ask me to state my name, date of birth, and why I am here.

I'm tempted to give a false name and date of birth, and say that I'm here for a manicure and pedicure, as long as they have that new shade of pink advertised in *Vogue*. They look so very serious, however, that I simply give them the information they requested. I realize if they are this serious, I'd better be a bit more somber myself.

Megan then attaches each chemo bag to its proper place on the pole, and each has its own controller that is set for the drip speed, time infused, and amount of the drug that will go into my veins. Prior to starting the infusion, Megan calls over yet another nurse to verify the drugs' names again as well as the speed, time, and overall amount to be infused.

For the first time, I realize just how serious this is and how dangerous these drugs really are. The nurses have every

part of their bodies covered in protective gear so nothing will touch their skin. I visibly gulp as I wonder what these deadly drugs will do to my body and organs. I have nothing to protect me except whatever strength my immune system can muster and my positive attitude that I can conquer this disease.

All I can do is watch as she presses the buttons to start the chemo. I am praying that I can be stronger than these highly hazardous drugs that are invading my body.

Home Sweet Home

My visits to Tunnell Cancer Center are somewhat less frequent these days. I now receive my scans and follow-up appointments with Dr. M every six months, but I still receive a port flush every six weeks. One would think that I would either be dreading those visits or at least be a bit anxious.

The truth is, however, when I walk through those doors now, I have a very different reaction.

I feel joy.

I feel safe.

I feel cared about.

I feel secure.

I feel strong.

I feel HOME.

Humble Warrior

Upright, hands at prayer
at my heart,
I lower forward
toward my bent knee
and rise up.
Once more, slowly,
and again   even
more   slowly.

I am reed, sapling,
a blade of grass,
a genuflection
of heart,
bowing
my small self
to the Lord of Creation,
the immense generosity of life.

Ellen Collins

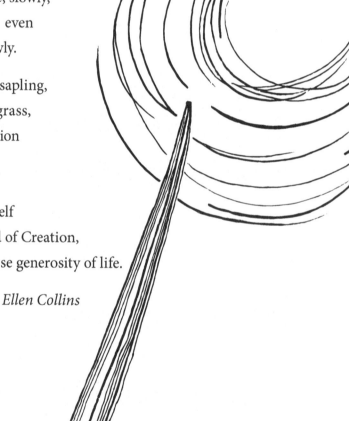

I Am a Rock Star?

When Peg left in the beginning of December 2018 to prepare and sell our Austin home, it freed up a lot of my time. I started to go to the gym for an hour or two every day. It was as much a social gathering as a work-out. Many of our friends used the same facility around the same time, and we would often work out together and chat before and after we finished. Since they all knew I would be alone for the next several weeks or maybe months, I also learned about events, got invited to private gatherings, and received invitations to nice home-cooked dinners.

I didn't really know Linda T very well prior to my daily gym regimen. She was in my "run-into-a-lot-but-don't-hang-with-hood." But she was also a daily gym-goer, and we would often chat about a myriad of topics. While I was on the treadmill, Linda often was on the Stairmaster machine, which was two rows directly in front of me. That's the one that mimics a real set of stairs, and both speed and tension can be adjusted. She went at a crazy pace with high tension and did all sorts of what appeared to be inhuman things, like going backwards, sideways, skipping stairs, hopping, running etc.

The Stairmaster was positioned near the front door, and many times as I was leaving, she was still on it. I would walk up beside her, give her a dirty look, growl and assume the Most Muscular Pose, one of the eight mandatory poses in bodybuilding competitions. She would crack up and fall out of rhythm on the Stairmaster, and play to be annoyed with me. "Yeah, yeah," she'd say, "You are a real gym rock star!"

The time after my cancer diagnosis was a tough emotional time for me to be alone. There were multiple necessary tests, procedures, and doctors' meetings prior to the lobectomy that produced fear and anxiety.

Most friends had no idea what to say or how to act around me. But going to the gym every day was my greatest pleasure, including even the day before my lobectomy. During those weeks from diagnosis to surgery, Linda became one of my steady and solid emotional foundations. She stuck with me from the beginning. Her demeanor was easy and honest. She never treated me with pity. She was never afraid to say the word cancer and talk about it. She was upbeat, energetic, and fun. She was a big part of why I always felt alive, happy, and positive when I was at the gym.

One day very near my operation, Linda said to me, "You know, Kim, you really are a Rock Star. Hmmmm… maybe not so much with the gym equipment, but certainly how you are handling all of this. You have lung cancer and a major operation pretty soon. You have no idea how all of this will turn out, and yet every day you walk in here strong and confident. You are always smiling and positive. Just remember through this experience that you ARE a Rock Star."

Two days before I had my pre-op appointment with Dr. W, my thoracic surgeon, Linda knocked at our door.

"Hey," Linda said. "I think it's really important that you show this lung surgeon who he is dealing with. I have something I think you should wear to the pre-op meeting." She pulled out a royal blue short-sleeved top with white lettering that said, *I Am A Rock Star.*

Linda

I absolutely loved it, and not only did I wear it to my pre-op appointment, I pointed to the lettering, looked sternly at him, and said, "Do you understand who you are dealing with?"

Dr. W let out a belly laugh and said, "I get the message loud and clear."

I wore that top constantly. And all through my recovery and chemotherapy, Linda was a very frequent visitor. She brought the neatest gifts—great reading materials, mind games, triple ginger cookies (my favorite), a little white lung cancer dog made of golf balls sold at the hospital, writing journals, more "I am a Rock Star" tops in different colors, rapper knit hats in case I lost my hair, joke books, jigsaw puzzles, word searches, a *uck cancer hot pink coffee cup, and on and on. And the best present of all was just sitting with me a few hours and chatting and laughing on those days Peg needed a break and went fishing with her friends.

I still love my "I am a Rock Star" tops, and wear them often in warm weather, but she was mistaken. *She* was—and remains—the Rock Star.

Inner Tubing

One of my most trying experiences was the chest tube placed in the upper area of my thoracic cavity after my operation. Normally having a chest tube is a one or two-day event. Then it is removed. For removal, my surgeon just needed to be sure that the fluid was no longer draining excessively. The lung needs to properly expand and have no air leaking. Otherwise, it could result in a pneumothorax (collapsed lung). At the end of the fourth day, however, I still had too much fluid drainage.

On all other levels, I was ready to be discharged and had been since the third day after my operation. By now, my surgeon, Dr. W, was more worried about me catching some sort of infection if I stayed in the hospital than about the dangers of going home with the chest tube.

I was okay with that. My wife, Peg, was given instructions on how to measure and dispose of the fluid held by the external receptacle, and I also had Visiting Nurses coming every other day to disinfect the equipment, clean the tube entrance and check the flow and color of the drainage. Keeping the chest tube in was painful, but I would rather have the pain than a collapsed lung from excess fluid buildup or a serious infection from staying in the hospital.

The apparatus did come with its own set of problems, however. I had to be really careful moving. It would be very easy to catch the external tube on a chair or end table. The tubing was also very long, and if I were going for a walk, I had to lift it up and carry it. Otherwise, it would get its own rhythm as I walked, and the pressure from that was excruciating. I also had to be extra careful it didn't get caught on any part of my walker. All that aside, I was determined I would walk at least twice a day, increasing the distance and speed every three or four days. But the most challenging activity was sleeping. I had to sleep flat on my back, place a chair next to the bedside, put the drainage receptacle and tubing on the chair and make sure I didn't move all night. If it fell to the floor, it would have ripped out of my chest. Also, getting in and out of bed with the contraption required a lot of help and finagling from Peg. These regimens lasted the first thirteen days I was home.

All that was tolerable, and I was determined to make the best of it. What I did NOT do well with was hearing from friends and neighbors about the absolutely excruciating pain of having the chest tube removed. I especially remember Jerry, who lived several houses down from us. He was a carpenter by trade, and a big strapping man. People from my home state of Maine would label him a "man's man." Nothing scared Jerry. Nothing made him flinch.

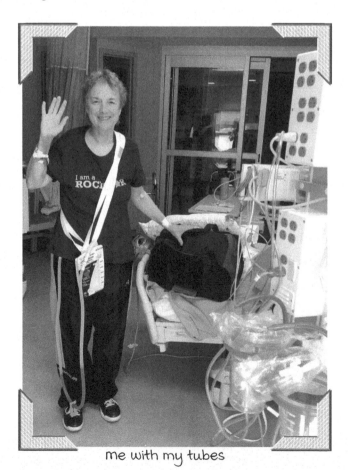

me with my tubes

So, one day Peg and I were taking our daily morning walk, and Jerry ran off his front porch and met us on the street. He first asked how I was, and without the slightest hesitation, he said, "You know, Kim, I was in a POW camp in Viet Nam, and I have had three extremely serious and painful operations. But I would take any of those experiences again before having some nurse pull out a chest tube. The pain was excruciating, and the doctor told me the next morning that I could be heard on the entire fourth floor of the hospital. It was also the first time in my life I cried."

How should one respond to that? I chose to give Jerry a big smile and we continued walking. That was the first nightmare I heard about chest tube removals. Several more horrific stories followed from at least a half a dozen other people. And all of them were as dramatic and frightening as Jerry's.

The day of the chest tube removal I was a mess. It was all I could do to even walk into the facility. Peg and I were escorted to one of the examination rooms, and Alice, one of Dr. W's Physician Assistants, said that she would remove the chest tube. I must have turned as white as the wall because she started telling me not to worry. It would only take a second and would not be painful, and that I should try to relax. I thought that maybe I could bargain with her. Let's keep it in two more weeks just be sure it was the right time to take it out. I thought she probably wouldn't bite for that excuse. I was only three feet from the door, and if I could be really fast, maybe I could get out the door before anyone could catch me.

Before I had finalized my escape plan, Alice said, "Kim, put your forehead on my forehead, and just concentrate on my eyes. I want you to take a deep breath, and I will remove the tube on the count of three." As I breathed in, I felt a searing burn deep in my chest that lasted no longer than a single second, and the tube was out. She smirked and said, "I didn't want you to have the three extra seconds of anxiety, so I pulled it when you breathed in."

I thought a lot about all the worrying and angst I went through, the night sweats of anxiety, the imagining myself screaming in pain, and what that pain would feel like. And yet once again, I was reminded that each of us travels our own road and has our own experiences. It's enough to worry or fret about those without the addition of making someone else's experiences our own. From that moment on, I came to rely on my own thoughts, feelings, and how I would face the coming challenges and situations versus those of others. My inner tube was out and my inner self was back.

Insanity

A famous philosopher once said, "Insanity is doing the same thing over and over again and expecting a different result."

I am not the brightest bulb, and what wattage I had certainly was dulled when I experienced all the twists, turns and bumps in the road of cancer. The journey was filled with many, many doctors' appointments, tests, and procedures. That didn't include, of course, all of the regular appointments I had to keep to stay overall healthy—primary care physician, gastro-intestinal, dermatologist, ophthalmologist, gynecologist, dentist, oral surgeon, otologist, allergist and the others that, at the moment, slip my mind.

Each and every one of those events and visits required that paperwork be completed. Many forewarned me to arrive at least thirty minutes in advance to fill out required information. And the minimum pre-time was usually fifteen minutes.

I tolerated this procedure for the first four or five visits to various medical facilities. But after that, I realized I was more stressed about finding, thinking about, and writing all this information over and over again than I was about any office visit or procedure I needed.

After filling out a very long pre-visit form of 12 pages at one doctor's office, I decided I was done with this nonsense. The minute I got home, I went upstairs to my study, fired up my lap-top, and wrote out all the pertinent information and inserted it into a chart. It took about three hours, but the time spent was worth it. When I checked in at a doctor's office and the receptionist would hand me the sheaf of papers to fill out, I would just hand over my chart. I remember the day the receptionist looked at it and gave me a big smile. "Just write on the front page 'See Attached' and sign on the bottom."

It was a great day for both of us.

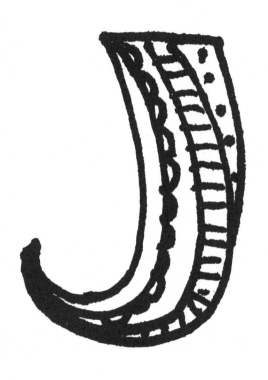

Jabberwocky

The first time I met Dr. M, my oncologist, she told me there were many types of lung cancer and many stages, progressions, and treatments for each one. "You have Stage 2B Invasive Adenocarcinoma, ACINI Predominant that's moderately differentiated," she said, "and it was completely excised. It was confined within the lung parenchyma. All margins were uninvolved but lymph nodes 10A and 10B exhibited metastatic adenocarcinoma. As far as visceral......" So far, I had listened to each and every word, but except for the words lung cancer, I didn't have a clue what she was talking about. Syllables were flying around the room, but none of them made sense.

My mind wandered to the time I brought the Chevy Equinox in for a rattle I heard in the front driver's side wheel area. They wanted to keep it for a day so they could do several test drives. The following afternoon, I received the call. "We found the issue," he said. And he proceeded to talk for a good five minutes. I understood three or four words at best, and when he came up for air, I simply asked him how much it would cost. I gulped at the price, but I really had no other choice but to pay if we wanted to remain a two-car family.

Invasive Adenocarcinoma,

ACINI Predominant

differentiated excised
confined parenchyma

margins uninvolved

lymph nodes

10A and 10B metastatic

adenocarcinoma
visceral...

When I noticed that Dr. M was staring at me and I was no longer hearing her voice, I simply asked when I could start chemotherapy. Although I had the complete pathology report, I didn't research the medical terms or look up the survival rate for my type and stage of lung cancer.

Here is what I knew. I had lung cancer. I planned to survive.

The term "jabberwocky" refers to the poem by the same name, written by Lewis Carroll and included in his book Through the Looking Glass, *published in 1871. The poem is largely composed of words that make no sense.*

Just Imagine

When I was told there was a good chance I would lose my hair, I tried to imagine what I would look like bald. Would I have one of those heads shaped like a globe? Be rather flat in the back? Have the start of a cone-head? Sport hills and valleys?

I hated the idea of a wig, so my friend Linda T bought me these great caps from Amazon like the rappers and young folks wear. Yup… I could live with that. I thought they were very cool, even though Peg, my wife, told me I looked like a Russian peasant.

Somehow my naturally thin, stringy hair stayed on my head through chemotherapy. One worry bit the dust!

Kindred Spirits

I was brought up with a deep and abiding belief in God and the devil, the glory of heaven and the agony of hell, and belief in saints and sinners. I went to Catholic elementary school, high school, and two years of an all-girls Catholic college. I was taught that ultimately God could be a punitive and vengeful God, and if I didn't follow the commandments and committed sins, I would face the fires of hell for eternity.

Through the years, I gradually stopped believing in many of the doctrines and creeds of the Catholic church, and I explored other less stringent religions, especially those that explained God as a kind, compassionate, loving, supportive and forgiving deity. No religion I visited, however, felt completely comfortable to me. So, for many, many years I didn't attend any form of religious or spiritual services.

But in mid-summer of 2018, I attended a Unitarian Universalist ceremony and really enjoyed it. It all started over a pancake. We were visiting with my friend, Carol H, and she mentioned that her church was putting on their annual all-you-can-eat breakfast, and the highlight was their "special pancakes." Since I'd never met a pancake I didn't like, I thought it was worth sitting through the fifty-minute service to sample these mystery delights.

They had me at hello. I was hooked on both the pancakes and the UUs. They were diverse and inclusive and believed in the inherent dignity of each person. They welcomed all genders and sexual orientations and all ethnic, racial and cultural backgrounds. They didn't care if you professed to atheism, Buddhism, Christianity, humanism, or any other belief.

I started going on a regular basis and even joined some of their groups. I was also a greeter on Sunday mornings, and no one gives hugs like the UUs. I enjoyed the services and the coffee hours with home-made delicacies and lively conversation. But most of all, I kept return-ing because they were just plain good people. They were kind, compas-sionate, fun-loving, passionately dedicated to local and world causes, and more than anything, they simply watched out for each other. No exceptions. No one was ever alone if you were a UU. And the irony was that although most of them did not believe in Christianity as a religion, they exhibited all of the traits that Christians believe are pure and good. I was home.

I have always believed that there is no such thing as a coincidence. Almost nine months later I had my first appointment with Dr. B, who suggested that even though I quit smoking fifteen years ago, I should get the free Medicare low-dose CT scan. The rest is history.

The UUs rallied like nothing I have ever experienced before or after my cancer. There were many, many cards. And because they knew this journey was not a short one, over time I received two or three cards from each person or couple. Every week I was listed in the pamphlet distributed as members entered the sanctuary, as well as in the online version. People were asked to pray or have positive thoughts for me. And that was for the many months I was ill. So many people called to wish me well and ask what I needed or what could they do to make my days easier. When I was able, I had visitors who would bring little gifts and cheer me up and make me laugh. I also was showered with won-derful homemade soups, casseroles, pies, cakes, cookies, and on and on. And when I was able to stand in front of the congregation and pro-fusely thank them for everything and tell them I was cancer-free, they gave me a standing ovation.

But more than anything, the UUs' love, support, and spiritual energy elevated my own spirit and gave me strength, courage, and positivity to conquer my illness. I felt brave and embraced by a beloved community. I will be indebted to each and every one of them for the rest of my life.

And to this day, I thank God that there are no coincidences.

Kiss of Death

One early Thursday morning in January 2021, I arrived for the CT scan portion of my scheduled check-up. Normally there are two short scanning sessions 10-15 seconds apart. This time, however, the technician requested that I wait before getting off the table. I then heard the machine rev up, and I went back in for another session.

When the third scan was completed, I sat up and glanced in the window where the technician operates the machine. There were four additional people intently staring at the screen. One was a man pointing at it, and the others all nodded. That was another first. Previously no one had ever been in that room except a single technician.

I instinctively knew something was wrong. No, everything was wrong. Why did I need three scans? Why were there several people in the technician's room, all concentrating on the screen? Was it a training session? Was the machine not working properly? Or were they analyzing the abnormality they saw on the scan?

I grabbed my things and rushed to my car. My insides felt ready to explode, my body was shaking, and my fingers were numb from holding the steering wheel so tight.

For the rest of the day, I called all the contacts I thought could get me the scan results. No one answered. I was left to wait it out on my own.

I spent hours pacing the floor, staring mindlessly out the window, and attempting to read a book and just seeing words on a page. My anxiety level was so high I could feel my heart pounding. I knew it was not good news.

Two o'clock came. Three o'clock came. Four o'clock came. Five o'clock came. Six o'clock came and went. Dear God, I would have to spend the night not knowing the bad news. But at 6:15 P.M. my cell phone rang. It was Alec, Dr. M's PA. He apologized for the delay. He told me that my scans showed no signs of cancer. I felt a hundred pounds of severe worry and angst leave my mind and body.

There are many lessons to learn from this experience. It will take me much time and thought to absorb all of them. But I do know this. Cancer didn't leave my mind or emotional system, even once I was declared in remission and "cancer-free." It will be always looming in the shadows until I am cleared by my next CT scan.

I also know I had already assigned myself the Kiss of Death. Fear of the unknown did, without a doubt, take over my reason and serenity, and abandon me in a place of darkness and dread. I wasted a beautiful day by needless fear and worry.

I promised myself I would work harder to live my mantra. No matter what situation comes my way. No matter what life brings. I will thrive.

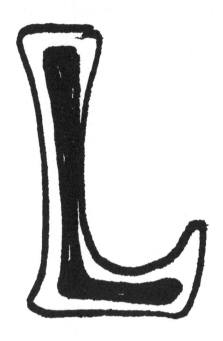

Lit Up Like a Christmas Tree

Peg and I are sitting in a room waiting to meet with Dr. W, my thoracic surgeon. There are two chairs in the corner. The room also has one of the massive machines that will show the PET scan results that will reveal whether the cancer has spread to other organs and parts of my body. Usually, I jabber when I am really nervous, but I am silent. Peg is always quiet. We sit and wait.

There is a light tap on the door, and in walk Dr. W's two Physician Assistants, Robin and Alice. Each carries a large piece of homemade German strudel on a paper towel. They tell us it is a gift from a grateful patient, and they hand a slice to each of us. It smells like heaven and tastes even better. I notice we are getting bits of strudel all over the carpeted floor. I'm hoping I won't get any on me and stain either my new bright blue "I am a Rock Star" T-shirt or my new brown checkered Vans sneakers. I wore both to impress Dr. W, hoping at this first meeting he would think I was pretty cool and maybe even brave.

As we eat the strudel, Robin and Alice talk about general things and ask us how long we've been in the area, where we live, and how we like Rehoboth Beach. In turn, they tell their stories. Robin relates that she and her wife just bought a house and are moving to the area. Then, Alice says, "We'll both be in the operating room every minute you are there, and you can call either of us, before or after the surgery, day or night." They hand Peg and me their cards which include their personal cell numbers. They act and sound like we are all old friends, and that they are sincerely interested in me and not just my medical issue. I feel my nervousness and anxiety lessen. The room feels bigger, and I am breathing better.

There is another light tap on the door, and in walks Dr. W. I am immediately drawn to his warm, caring eyes and his big smile. I feel an instant connection with him, and I already feel safe in his hands.

"Hi, I'm Dr. W." He looks at my shirt and says, "And I guess you are a Rock Star."

"Allow me to correct you," I say. "I am THE Rock Star who is also sporting brand-new Vans sneakers."

He starts to laugh, gives me a fist bump, and says, "How about if we look at your PET scan?" He presses a button and says, "If you look at this slide, you can see that most of it is pretty dark. That means everything is okay." He then points to the alien and moves his finger over different parts of the alien's body and legs. "Now take a look at this. It's all lit up like a Christmas tree. This is what I'll remove from your lung."

I look at the alien for what feels like a very long time. It's much lighter than the surrounding area. I try to imagine it with strings of

multi-colored lights, silver tinsel, and lots of decorative ornaments hanging from its long, spindly, and disfigured legs. But all I see is the grotesque, ugly, and ominous thing that has invaded my body.

"What about the enlarged lymph node?" I ask. I don't dare refer to it as the space ship.

"No Christmas lights on that puppy. It's just an ordinary lymph node. Lots of folks have enlarged lymph nodes. It's nothing to worry about."

I make one last attempt to picture the alien decorated as a Christmas tree and realize it is an impossible task. But I am at least grateful to know the space ship is not alive and is nothing to worry about.

I am even more grateful to know that I am placing my life in the hands of this incredibly warm and supportive medical team. They really care about me. I somehow know it will be okay. Perhaps Christmas has come early this year.

Little Things

Cancer isn't so much a disease as it is a lifestyle. There are numerous follow-up tests, scans, and procedures that normally occur for a very long time—maybe forever—even after being declared cancer-free.

There were two reasons I was particularly apprehensive prior to one particular round. First, lung cancer has a very high rate of return, and this six-month interval test and bloodwork were the longest I'd been without being checked medically. The prior intervals had been four months. Second, with the contrast CT scan, an iodine-based dye is injected into my body via a vein or chest port. It requires fasting and swallowing a liquid that is the consistency of mucous. It also tastes bad. In addition, it is rough on the kidneys, so bloodwork must be completed prior to the procedure, as well as drinking lots of water two days before the scan. And the procedure itself is uncomfortable.

Mary Jo introduced herself as my technician. As I lay on the table, we chit-chatted while she connected the IV mechanism to my port. She told me she had done this work for over thirty years, most of it at Beebe.

mary Jo

"Okay," she said. "Everything is all set. Would you please place your arms over your head?" She was now positioned behind me and out of sight. After I raised my arms, she quietly asked, "Are you ready for me to inject the dye?"

"Yes," I sighed. I wasn't looking forward to the injection. I remembered that it stings and feels hot.

All of a sudden, as I felt the liquid enter my port and dreaded the burning sensation that was coming, I also felt a hand holding mine. It was warm and strong, and I squeezed it tighter as the dye started to sting. I saw the room's bright lights, heard the loud whirr of the machine, but most of all, I felt Mary Jo's hand. I've had other contrast CT scans, but for the first time, I wasn't going through this experience alone.

For over thirty years Mary Jo has been administering this scan. She has given hundreds, probably even thousands, in her long career. Giving her heart and compassion to a nervous patient certainly was not part of the job description. And yet, she was sympathetic enough, caring enough, and thoughtful enough to make an anxious patient's day a whole lot easier and certainly not so scary.

There are many acts of greatness that we hear about daily. There are also small acts of kindness that will never be forgotten by the fortunate people who receive them. I am one of those very fortunate people. Thank you forever, Mary Jo, for making a not so pleasant day a positive day to remember.

Loneliness

Sometimes,
though rare,
either surrounded
by people
or in my own quiet moment,
I felt alone,
with lung cancer
as my only
companion.

Lung Cancer Facts and Statistics

Here's what you need to know.

- Lung cancer is the LEADING CAUSE OF CANCER DEATHS among both men and women.
- Each year, MORE PEOPLE DIE OF LUNG CANCER than of colon, breast, and prostate cancer combined.
- The American Cancer Society predicts that in 2022, there will be 236,180 NEW LUNG CANCER CASES, 117,910 in men and 118,830 in women.
- For the same year, 130,180 DEATHS ARE PREDICTED.
- ONE IN 15 MEN and ONE IN 17 WOMEN will get lung cancer in their lifetime.

ESTIMATED LUNG CANCER STATISTICS IN THE U.S. (2022) TOTAL: 236,180

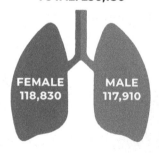

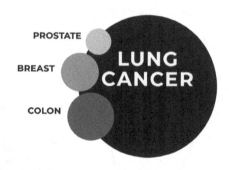

Mailbox Mile

After my lobectomy operation, I was convinced that walking would help me heal quickly. The first time I walked, I used my walker with wheels and tennis balls. I made it three mailboxes. The first couple of weeks were very tough because I still had my chest tube in to drain thoracic fluid. It was incredibly painful but necessary.

Over time, I was able to walk fifteen mailboxes. Then I could walk five mailboxes without the walker. Soon I was obsessed with the goal of walking the one-mile perimeter of our development as soon as possible. I started really looking forward to the daily walk, and each day doing at least three mailboxes better than the day before.

It was so fun and exciting to challenge myself. The day I walked the mile without the walker and touched the very last mailbox was one of my best memories ever.

Maine Mug

I was born and bought up in central Maine. I love its rugged terrain, independent people, and open spaces. I also love everything that makes it famous and a favorite state for tourists—lobsters, lighthouses, rocky Atlantic coastlines, moose, and blueberries.

No matter where I lived, I always made both an annual winter and summer trip home to visit family and tour parts of Maine that were either favorites or sites that I had not yet explored. Unfortunately, in the summer of 2019 I was receiving chemotherapy treatments and could not go home.

One day in July, Maureen K called me and asked if she could drop by the house for a few minutes. She had just returned from a Maine vacation and bought me a little gift from my home state.

It was a coffee mug. But it wasn't just any mug. It was a mug that fit my small hands perfectly. It also held just the right amount—not so much that it would cool too quickly and not so little that I'd need a refill.

But the best thing was what was written on it.

maureen

I am brave

I am healing

I am blessed

She gave me the mug almost three years ago. I still use it every morning and read the words every day. Some days when all is good, it helps me feel gratitude and joy. On days that aren't so good, the words give me strength, hope, and feelings of positivity.

Such a little gift with such maximum impact.

Major Drinking Problem

During chemotherapy, I had a drinking problem.

It wasn't what you expect. It was not drinking enough. No matter how hard I tried, it seemed impossible. I never had been a big or even a normal drinker. And water was always the hardest for me.

Water is one of the "must do's" of chemotherapy. So, not only was it critical for me to stay hydrated, but the more water I drank, the quicker the chemo toxins would flush out of my body. And the doctor, nurses, and I absolutely wanted that to happen as soon as possible.

To compound the situation, I also had gastrointestinal issues even prior to the cancer—IBS, acid reflux, and diverticulosis. So, I wasn't allowed any liquid with seltzer or any kind of bubbles, nor citrus, caffeine, tea, chocolate, and several other tasty things that would have helped me drink large quantities of liquids.

The further along I got with the chemo infusions, the less appetite I had. The less appetite I had, the harder it was to swallow. It felt like I had just finished a huge second helping of Thanksgiving dinner and my mother was insisting I eat more. I felt filled up right to the top of my throat.

So, no matter how hard I tried to drink, it just didn't always happen. Consequently, I would get dehydrated. The triage nurses suggested drinking before I ate, and that should allow me to drink more water. But when I did that, I was too full to eat even the things I still liked, and I started to lose a lot of weight.

Although my chemotherapy drugs were very harsh, the medicines prescribed to counteract the side effects worked very well. I actually was the sickest when I would get dehydrated. I felt dizzy and had weakness in my legs, difficulty breathing, rapid heartbeat, and a headache.

As soon as I got these symptoms, I would call Triage. The nurse would quickly set me up with a saline infusion appointment. Thank goodness for saline solution. After an hour at the infusion center, I was a new person.

I still think about the irony of that situation. The harsh chemo drugs did not make me terribly ill. My drinking problem caused the most angst and illness. Interestingly enough, it still does.

Menu Mania

One of the sections I read in my Beebe Cancer Manual said that it is common for patients to experience changes in food preferences. My mother used to joke that if she warmed up cardboard and poured a little Hershey's syrup on it, I would have no problem eating it. That was a bit of a stretch, but since there wasn't anything except lamb that I couldn't eat with great enthusiasm, I wasn't too worried about that side effect.

As my treatments progressed, however, I was really surprised at what happened. After my second chemo treatment, I was watching a television ad for a big, fat, juicy Wendy's hamburger, one of my favorite foods. I literally felt so sick that I had to walk out of the room. I could even smell the grease over the airwaves.

Here are some of the food shifts I experienced.

PRE-CHEMO	DURING CHEMO
Eggs cooked any way (hard-boiled, scrambled, sunny-side up, over easy, soft-boiled, quiche, meringue).	Pancakes with lots of extra butter and syrup (I preferred Aunt Jemima with added cinnamon, drowning in very hot Vermont maple syrup). Anything short of this tasted like phlegm.
Medium-rare to rare N.Y. strip steak smothered in grilled green peppers and onions. A big, fat, medium rare burger loaded with Heinz catsup and raw onions. The juicier the better!	Pan-fried cube steak and packaged ham cooked to the consistency of cardboard. The smell of either of them cooking made me nauseous. Swallowing more than a few bites was a miracle.
Anything Italian. Chicken parm, lasagna, ravioli, pasta with Bolognese sauce, calamari, linguine with clam sauce, pizza.	Aunt Annie's macaroni shells with white cheddar, practically tasteless. The white sauce didn't remind me of blood. I ate it one small shell at a time. If that didn't work, I went for pre-made store-bought mashed potatoes.

Burritos, chalupas, enchiladas, fajitas, tacos, tostados, guacamole and refried beans, warm sopapillas.	Pop tarts (cinnamon only) that were sold at the Dollar Tree store. They had to be nibbled from the outside in. I was afraid I couldn't handle the explosion of flavor if I dived into the sugary middle.
Desserts—you name it! Anything that included at least a half cup of sugar in the recipe. Candy in all its forms. First choice chocolate, followed by black and red licorice.	The appearance of chocolate inspired unsavory reminders. My go-to became an extra-large Dairy Queen milkshake with an infusion of double peanut butter. I often used one as a substitute for a regular meal.

For quite a while, everything tasted metallic. Finally, I was slowly able to tolerate and even like more of the food groups. And within five months after chemo, I was able to look at, smell, and taste most of my pre-chemo diet.

I still have a hard time with eggs, though. I eat them now and then, but I miss our former intimate relationship.

My Mantra

Mantras originated in the practices of Hinduism and Buddhism. Originally a mantra was a meaningful word or sound that had two functions: to instill within the reciter a particular spiritual doctrine, and to serve as a vehicle for meditation. In today's world, the definition is much broader. It now can be a phrase that is repeated by someone who is praying or even an affirmation to motivate and inspire one to be their best self. It also can affirm how one wants to live their life.

So why the hoopla about the history and definition of a mantra? Discovering I had lung cancer and learning it was the number one killer annually of all types of cancers was a very stressful and surreal time for me. I kept trying to wrap my head around the reality of it all and continually thought about my own mortality. Friends tried to help and console me but often made it worse by telling horror stories of family members or friends who died of lung cancer. Most were difficult and painful struggles. Television and radio ads about lung cancer were also terribly frightening. No matter where I went or what I was doing, I seemed bombarded by the horror and death that surrounded lung cancer.

I knew that I desperately needed a mantra. I knew that, with intention, I needed to re-connect with my heart's deepest longing, to be safe and filled with strength, light, and hope. I was losing the core essence of my life, and I innately knew I would not survive what was to come without it.

I also knew I needed to talk to Debbie D, my dear friend, who became my spiritual advisor. I gave her examples of remarks and events I experienced and told her that when one of those things occurred, I felt really afraid, in darkness, and totally out of control. To me, those feelings were actually as frightening as the disease itself. "Kim," Debbie said, "everyone has their own individual journey. All these things that you described to me are real and true. But they are NOT your reality and truth. You have your own journey that only God knows. Your part is to live in the light every day that you are given, and fill it with hope, joy and gratitude."

I thought about this a lot. I knew the remarks and events I had been experiencing would continue in the future. I couldn't change life's realities. But I could change my response and feelings to those remarks and events. And I did. So, whenever my world started to sink into fear and darkness, I would say my mantra. It was and remains:

THAT IS NOT MY JOURNEY. THIS IS MY JOURNEY. AND I WILL THRIVE.

In the last two and a half years of my life, I have said my mantra hundreds of times. And each time it awakens my true self and life intention—to rise above fear and darkness and live with hope, light, and serenity.

This is my journey. And I will thrive.

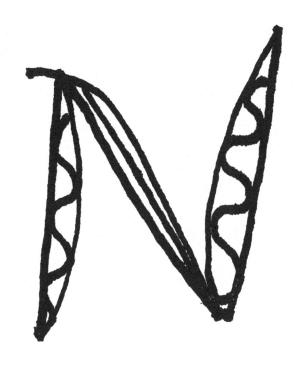

News Flash

When I was first diagnosed, Peg didn't seem to want to talk about my cancer. I honestly thought she didn't care. I was very wrong.

I learned this by a behavior she exhibited a few weeks after my diagnosis. Whenever we saw a friend or neighbor, or she was on the phone with one of her friends, or we met someone new, as soon as there was an opening, she would suddenly blurt out, "Kim has lung cancer!" Then she would nod.

And suddenly, it hit me that she was as numb about this as I was. Saying the words out loud to another person was the only way she knew how to make it a reality.

No Easy Way

There's no easy way to wrap one's ahead around the news that you have cancer. All you know is that life as you have known it for the past sixty-nine years is over. You don't know what to say. You don't know where to go. You don't know what to do.

You are basically a walking empty shell, and you are about to enter a world completely foreign to anything you have ever known.

Number 5

The Beebe Bookhammer Outpatient Center is located in Rehoboth Beach and is in the same complex as Beebe's Tunnell Cancer Center. The campus is only a little over a mile from my home. During the pre-op testing, post-op care of my lobectomy, and chemotherapy, I was a frequent visitor to both of these facilities. I also received and continue to receive all of my imaging (x-rays, PET scans, regular and contrast CT scans, mammograms, and sonograms) and bloodwork in these two facilities.

Bookhammer reminds me of a well-run airport. Inside the front door, there is a circular desk where two women sit. They are prompt, friendly, and professional. You are initially checked in by name and test to be conducted, receive any paperwork you may have to complete prior to the procedure, and given a pager. When the pager vibrates, it displays a number from 1 to 9. They are so organized that I never had time to complete my paperwork before my pager vibrated and directed me to one of the nine cubicles, where I was processed to receive my procedure.

Cherae

Here is the interesting part. Over the last two and a half years, I can't even begin to imagine how many times I've used the services in this building. It has to be at least forty visits. And at all but less than a handful of those times, my pager buzzed the number 5 booth. I'm not a mathematician, but even I know that the odds of this coincidence are astronomical.

When I am anxious or afraid, I tend to chatter, or try to be funny. So, I had become familiar with Cherae in Booth 5. And in fun, every time I would see her, instead of saying her name, I would call her Number 5. She also had a great sense of humor, and enjoyed our exchanges.

There was one day in particular, however, that was a very serious visit. On April 12, 2019, I arrived at Bookhammer for my first PET scan. The results would determine if the cancer had spread to other parts of my body. I was admittedly a wreck. I had come to grips with the lung cancer, and I felt that I could handle it with my support system, my faith, and my serenity. But the thought of cancer throughout my body was incredibly frightening. So, on that day, I was somber and quiet, and Number 5 picked up on it immediately. Not wanting to intrude, she started asking me for the information she needed to process my visit.

After two or three questions, I finally put my hand on hers and said, "Number 5, I'm getting a test today that will tell me if the lung cancer has spread to other parts of my body. I'm really afraid. Will you pray for me?"

Without hesitation, Number 5 said, "Yes, I will pray for you." She squeezed my hand hard between her own two hands. "But I already know that the cancer has not and will not spread. You will be okay. I will also have my church pray for you until you are through with this illness." Her eyes were steady and piercing. She believed that, and I believed her.

As I write this essay, it's over two years later. Three days ago, I went to get my five-month CT scan at Beebe's Bookhammer. And, yes, once again, I looked at my pager vibrating, and up popped the number 5. I sat down in front of Charae's cubicle, and I tried really hard to look and sound up and positive. We were now old friends who had been fighting and winning this battle for over two years.

"I'm here to get my five-month scan to see if I am still cancer free," I said. "I'm going to be okay. Aren't I, Number 5?"

She squeezed my hand. "You are STILL cancer free, and you will STAY cancer free."

I nodded and gave her a really big smile. After all, who was I to question a woman who was so sure of what reality is and will remain?

When I arrived home, I Googled the significance of the number 5. It is a symbol of the goodness and grace of God. It is also a very powerful number sent by the angels if you are in need of their help or assistance. When receiving the number 5, your guardian angel is also trying to tell you that many changes are coming into your life and will be good for you.

Coincidence? I think NOT.

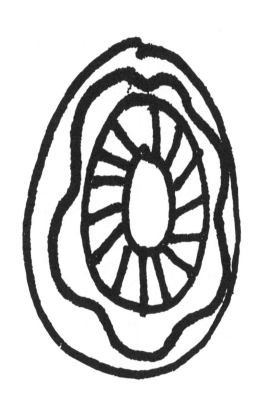

Obnoxious

I think I mentioned that I had never had an operation except a childhood tonsillectomy. So, I truly had no idea what to expect before, during, or after the lobectomy. All I knew was that cutting out the tumor from my right lung was considered a "major and serious" operation, and I would be recouping in the ICU.

I decided to take this operation one day at a time, and not fret about something that might never happen, or that would be interpreted or felt differently by someone else. After receiving much unsolicited, frightening misinformation regarding my medical procedures from well-meaning friends and strangers, I decided to discuss the operation with no one. I knew I would be far calmer if I followed that path.

So, I woke up after the surgery, and the first thing I saw was Peg standing next to my bed. She looked a little nervous and uncomfortable. Catherine, the nurse standing next to her

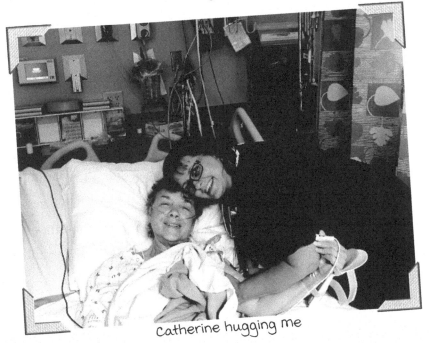

Catherine hugging me

seemed quite amused, with a big smile on her face. I quickly looked around the room, and realized Peg was the only person who was NOT a patient or a nurse. The patients all seemed to be moaning and groaning, and the nurses appeared to be trying to comfort them.

Catherine laughed. "Well, at last you've calmed down a little and aren't yelling any more. You were causing quite a ruckus in here."

"Is it time for lunch?"

Catherine patted my knee, snickered, and said, "I'll be back with some water in a bit."

"I'm not supposed to be in here," Peg said. "Catherine said you were yelling at the top of your lungs that you wanted your wife. No matter what they did, you wouldn't stop. This is the initial recovery room, and no visitors are allowed."

"But you're in here," I said.

"Only because you wouldn't shut up, and even the medications didn't help."

Shortly after, Catherine returned with some water. I told her I was sorry I had made so much noise and asked Peg to take our picture together. After Peg took the photo, Catherine helped me drink a few sips of water and then injected something in my IV.

That's the last thing I remember. Peg said they upped my meds, and soon I was out like a light until I woke up the next morning in the ICU. Peg later told me that she left shortly after for a nice, quiet evening at home.

The lesson to be learned is that if you have a major operation, you may well wake up in the recovery room and yell like a banshee or do some other obnoxious behavior. It might be the effects of the anesthesia. So, it probably wasn't your intent. At least that's the excuse I would use.

Only a Memory

I met Debbie D at a group dinner after a play. We sat across from each other and started chatting. She worked at the National Institutes of Health in Washington, DC, Monday through Friday, and owned a home locally in Milton that she used on weekends, holidays, and down time. She told me that when family or friends were very ill or terminal, she would help prepare them to cross over to the other side.

I had just learned that I had lung cancer, and at that point, I didn't know if it had metastasized to any other part of my body. I was also pretty frightened about my chances of surviving this horrific disease. But when this very analytical woman who approves research funding for various high-level medical initiatives told me that she helped people cross over to the other side, I knew that our meeting was no coincidence. From that night on, Debbie became a constant in my life, and we met on many, many Sundays for breakfast at a local diner. She became not only a close friend but also my spiritual advisor.

I was very blessed to have only a few really bad days and not much scary news during my cancer experience. But when I did, I would always visit, call, or text Debbie. Debbie was my go-to for those times that I felt

Debbie

weak emotionally or spiritually, or when I had a tough physical day during chemotherapy. I could waver with Debbie. I could be weak with Debbie. I could feel lost with Debbie. I could tell Debbie I was losing my faith. I could share with Debbie that I was really sick and felt horrible.

In her calm and caring way, she would talk me through whatever it was that had me down or afraid. She always ended the meeting, call, or text with the same message. "Kim, soon this will only be a memory. Remember today will only be a memory."

And writing this over two years later, I realize she was right.

Outing Myself

I hung up from Dr. B, my primary care physician, and every part of my body and mind felt numb. I couldn't move. I couldn't talk. I couldn't think. The low-dose CT machine showed two abnormalities in my chest. I had a 1.3 centimeter spiculated nodule in the right upper lobe and a large abnormal lymph node in the middle of my chest. What did that mean? How long had I had them? Did they come as a package or did they appear at different times? Why hadn't I been sick or felt pain? My mind was whirring with a million questions. Instead I stayed silent. Dr. B told me they would arrange an appointment with a pulmonologist who would read the scan and determine next steps.

I needed to call Peg in Austin, but I didn't think I could form the words, and it was too early to call there. And tonight was card night. We were a group of women who played Hand and Foot every Thursday evening. We rotated homes and took a break in the middle of the game for snacks and chatter. Dear God, how would I ever make it through tonight? Right now, I couldn't even think that far ahead. I really wanted a cup of coffee, but it seemed too complicated a task. So, I just sat and stared at the corn field behind the house.

About two hours later, when I could finally minimally function, I called Peg and told her. We were silent for a long time. Finally, she said, "We'll get through this." We both knew we didn't have a choice. We talked about who to tell at this phase, and both felt it was too early for family and most friends, but that our card group would be perfect. We loved this group. We are all so very different but so deeply connected at our cores. We have shared much joy and sorrow together throughout the years, and in my heart, I knew that each person in this group would provide needed love and strength in their own unique way. I knew I'd need the company and support, especially with Peg in Austin for the next several weeks.

When I had worked, I was a speaker and a trainer, but somehow, I couldn't seem to figure out what to say. It seemed like such an easy thing to do. Just say because you were an ex-smoker, your PCP sent you for a free low-dose CT scan. The results were abnormal. You have a spiculated nodule and an enlarged lymph node. You will see a pulmonologist to determine next steps.

How difficult was that? I had actually timed it and practiced several times. Fifteen seconds to say the words at a normal conversational pace. Fifteen seconds to make this massive change in my life real, not only to myself but now to an important part of my world. Still, there was a part of me that felt I shouldn't even tell the card group. I wondered if it would all go away if I didn't tell anyone. Maybe if I didn't say the words out loud, the nodule and lymph node would never become realities. I thought of Alice in Wonderland falling through the rabbit hole. Once I said the words, there would be no turning back. But I knew with Peg still in Austin, I would need the comfort and support of this group.

I walked in Mary's door to laughter and hugs. Everyone was in a great mood, and we finally settled down to some serious cards. I was very distracted and nervous, but tried to hide my feelings behind laughter and jokes.

Snack time came quicker than I wanted, and it was now or never. "Okay," I said. "I have some news I would like to share with you all." I said my four sentences slowly and exactly as I had practiced them. I wondered if I went over or under my fifteen second target.

I saw eyes get huge, mouths drop, and tears on some cheeks. Some immediately got up and hugged me. A few just stared at the wall or out the window. The rest just looked down at the table and grimaced like they were in pain. And as they each breathed in my message in the best way they knew how, I breathed in each of their reactions. I was glad I had outed myself. I knew I was not alone for wherever and however long this journey would take me.

Pain

I think I have a high tolerance for pain. In my thirties, I had a severe case of bi-lateral Temporomandibular Joint (TMJ) disorder. The doctor said the arthroscopic surgery would require a recuperative period of six weeks minimum, and each jaw should be repaired separately. I convinced the oral surgeon to do both jaws the same day. I was back to work in a week.

I'd never had major surgery, and I really didn't know what pain was involved with a lung operation and chemotherapy. I started the process with an open mind. I knew the lobectomy would probably be painful, and I'd heard from multiple friends and other sources that chemotherapy could also get nasty.

I chose not to research either the lobectomy or the chemotherapy since I had no choice about undergoing either one. I decided I wouldn't waste time and emotion on the fear and apprehension that every test, procedure, and treatment would be painful. I reminded myself that whatever pain I had would be treated by a great medical team who would help me to live and beat the odds.

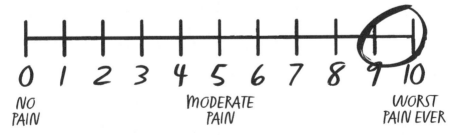

For the record, the lobectomy was pretty painful for the first several months. I had a lot of numbness in my abdomen and side, some intense nerve pain, and some muscle pain when I tried to do certain movements.

As I write this, over two years later, I still have some numbness and get nerve pain if I strain my right side or move in certain ways. The doctors told me that this may be residual and might not disappear. If that's the case, it's a pain I can live with. The only other bad pain I experienced was gastrointestinal pain during chemotherapy. I have IBS, and the chemotherapy caused some pretty difficult times. But all in all, the pain I experienced was tolerable, and the majority of it lasted only a short period of time.

I think our mind also plays a strong role in pain management. I believe that the more we worry and obsess about future pain, the more pain we will experience when it arrives. Best of all, if we choose NOT to obsess and fret about pain, the happier we will be and the more time we will have to enjoy our lives.

Peg

My wife Peg and I are like oil and water, salt and pepper, day and night. She is calm, quiet, and reticent, and she never worries about anything until it actually happens. Her one fault, self-admittedly, is she is a horrible procrastinator. I, on the other hand, am not calm, not quiet, and definitely not reticent. I am your quintessential Type A who gets the job done before you even realize that there is a job to do. My biggest fault is being way too impatient and jumping the gun needlessly.

There were times in my journey, however, when I lost my way or was afraid, and worse yet, didn't have the words or emotional strength to express what I was feeling. It was in those times that Peg, my wife and caretaker, would carry me through. It wasn't with words or long discussions. She never asked me how I was feeling, especially when I was feeling badly. She never hovered over me or fed my dramatic side. That wasn't her way. She knew my nature well enough to know that I was better off NOT talking about or focusing on my illness. Instead, she showed her love and caring with the things she did. She would have me focus on something else, like a good movie, friends visiting, playing some gin rummy, or taking me for a long ride in the car. Or if she really wanted to lighten my mood, she would make her special pancakes laced with vanilla and cinnamon.

Peg was always deeply and quietly concerned. She did copious research and reading about lung cancer (mine in particular), lobectomies, and chemotherapy. I had made up my mind I would focus on positive things and also trust my doctors. I walked into each phase of my cancer with light, hope, and faith. I deeply believed that this was my journey, and I was not a statistic or an average. When I needed to know something, however, she told me in "Kim talk" (no drama, just facts, ma'am). And when I felt really good, she celebrated with me.

I know that in many ways she suffered far more than I did. All she could really do was stand by and watch me

me and Peg

go through the process and make me as comfortable as possible. It's my belief that her job was far worse than anything I, as a cancer patient, might have ever experienced. She had to watch a feisty, strong, and upbeat spouse be afraid, or sick, or exhausted, knowing she couldn't fix anything. She had to bite her tongue when I snapped at her or when she cooked a delicious meal that was my favorite and I just turned my head away because the sight and smell of it made me sick. And she had to be present almost all the time because there were so many things I couldn't do for myself anymore. And worst of all, her life was so deeply entrenched with all the facets of my cancer (doctors' appointments, tests, operations, chemotherapy sessions, trips to the pharmacy, shopping for special food) month after month that there was little time for what used to be a life of her own.

After this experience, I have great empathy for anyone who is saddled with the role of primary caretaker. And if any caretaker should receive a medal, my wife, Peg is at the front of the line.

Thank you, Peg, for all you did during that long and difficult period. I will be forever grateful and indebted to you.

Pillow Talk

I remember waking up in agony the morning after my surgery. Each breath exploded in sharp pain and a deep throbbing. My entire right side felt on fire. The pain was so bad it was blue. I can't explain why it had a color. I just knew it was living in the right side of my body and it was blue. I tried to touch the spot where it was becoming unbearable, and as I moved my arm, I noticed an IV needle in my wrist wrapped in tape and a plastic tube sticking out of the middle of my right side. I wanted to pull both the needle and the tube out, but somehow, I knew that would be the wrong thing to do.

I could hear voices, but they seemed soft and far away. I turned my head to the left and gazed at an empty bed. Above it was a circular rod with a heavy curtain attached. I heard footsteps to my right, and as I turned, a very pretty nurse with the nametag "Jen" walked up to my bedside, smiled and asked me how I was feeling. "Am I in a hospital?" l asked.

"Yes," she responded. "You had a lobectomy late yesterday afternoon and you are in the ICU ward of Beebe Hospital."

"The ICU ward? That's a big deal," I said.

"Well, you're a big deal," she laughed. I started to laugh too, but when I did, I thought my whole right side would disintegrate.

Jen told me that it was time for my medication and I would feel a whole lot better in a few minutes. She also said I would be very sleepy, and sleep was going to be my best friend for the next couple of days. As she moved to the other side of the bed to check my IV, I noticed a rectangular pillow at the bottom of the bed. It was about two feet long and a little under a foot wide, and each of the four corners had an orange tassel attached. On the front of the pillow six little colorful birds sat on what looked like a green branch.

Sue

Jen noticed I was looking at the pillow and said, "Your friend, Sue, dropped off this pillow very early this morning." She went on to explain that thoracic surgeries (hearts and lungs) are very painful. Most hospitals have heart-shaped red pillows for patients to hug, and it helps to stabilize the chest and relieve some of the pain. She said she had never seen a pillow for lung surgery, but that Sue had looked all over town for a special pillow for me. She finally found this one at Pier One. She pointed out that it was longer and narrower than the heart pillows and would fit me perfectly. Jen smiled again, injected pain medication into my IV, picked up the pillow, positioned it perfectly on my chest and wrapped my arms around it. The last thing I remembered I was smiling.

I've never felt a strong attachment to a pillow, but my bird pillow became my best friend for the next several weeks. Hugging it alleviated so much pressure in my chest and my side, and no matter which way I moved, it helped to eliminate a significant amount of pain. The cover also went in the washing machine several times, and it always retained its beautiful colors.

Once I no longer needed the pillow for pain and help sleeping, I placed it on a chair in the family room. Higgins, our dog, then decided it would become his favorite napping pillow. So, there it still sits for both of us to enjoy. It will always remain a most precious gift that helped me through a difficult period of my recovery.

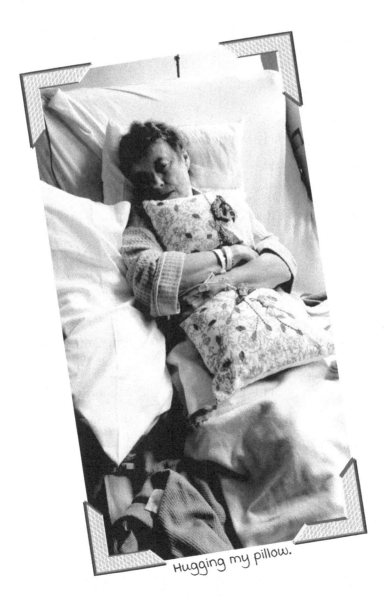

Hugging my pillow.

Prayer Power

When I got cancer, I asked people to pray for me. I learned that people have very different ideas about what God is and how to pray to this entity that is so much greater than anything we can imagine. I've learned many things about prayers. They may be pre-set words. They may be crossing your fingers, throwing a penny in a fountain, whistling on a walk in the woods, dancing alone around a fire, drumming in unison to the beat of others, singing, playing a musical instrument, or just plain positive thoughts.

I've also learned that prayer emanates from our soul and expresses itself in as many ways as humans can express themselves. But ultimately all manifestations of prayer at its core are intentions that are directed to and connected with a universal source far more powerful than we can imagine.

That power can move mountains, stop wars, conquer disease, save love, and forgive the greatest of sins. And when prayers from groups of people connect for the same cause or need, miracles are born.

During my cancer, I was blessed with so very many individuals and groups praying for me. It changed my life. I was filled with serenity, peace, love, and faith, and I was able to discover a direct connection with the source of what I call God. I still don't understand who or what he or she or it is, but I know that the united and intended prayer energy of so many people saved my life. It was cancer's gift to me. And I will be forever grateful.

Quandary Time

Dr. M, my oncologist, believed that the lobectomy eradicated all of the existing cancer. I did have two lymph nodes where the cancer had metastasized, but the nodes were located next to the tumor. The remaining six distal lymph nodes were clean, and no other signs of cancer were apparent on my PET scan. So, in cancer terms, I was in "remission" on May 16th, 2019, at the completion of my lobectomy.

Dr. M also told me that the five-year survival rate for my specific type of lung cancer was 56%. If I chose to have chemotherapy, that would raise my rate by 5%, with a new percentage total of a 61% chance of making the five-year survival rate. In cancer terms, I would be rewarded with being able to call my cancer "cured."

The negative was that the drugs for lung cancer were severe and harsh and most likely would cause some permanent damage to my body, including additional gastrointestinal issues as well as chemo brain.

There were many opinions on both sides of the fence—by medical folks as well as family and friends. But I knew ultimately the choice was mine. I chose chemotherapy. As a result, I have several of the side effects of chemo brain. Some effects are more severe than others. My pre-cancer gastrointestinal issues definitely have exacerbated post-chemotherapy. And I often feel fatigued, especially when I don't drink enough water.

I don't regret my choice, however. I wanted to live, and I have given myself the best possible odds of doing that.

This is my journey, and I will thrive.

Quit Listening

After Dr. B called me and told me that I had a tumor on my right lung, the parade of appointments, tests and procedures began. It seemed that I had something almost every day.

The first and most critical was the PET scan. I didn't know much about the PET but I knew one of its main functions was to determine if cancer had spread to other parts of the body. I quickly found out that many people had an opinion about this scan and offered words of advice. Here are a few of the many:

- It's a machine that they slide you into, and it is really close to your face *(ugh)*

- If you're the least bit claustrophobic, you'd better ask your doctor for a valium and get an eye mask *(so I did both)*

- The sound is very loud and disturbing, so you might want to bring earphones because it takes over an hour *(yup...they are ready to go)*

- They IV you with radioactive dye and you must sit perfectly still for an hour. You should bring a book or magazine *(packed in my satchel)*

I was already frightened that the cancer may have spread to other parts of my body. Now I was also very anxious about the procedure itself. By the time I arrived for the appointment, I was a wreck.

I was in the waiting room for fifteen minutes, and when the door opened and Laura M called my name, my legs started shaking. We walked down a long corridor and passed several medical offices along the way. Each step was harder and harder to take. We finally turned a corner, and she opened the door to a small, pleasant room. Janine A smiled and introduced herself.

"Should I take my valium now?" I looked at both women and they glanced at each other.

Janine smiled again. "I see you've been educated on the PET scan."

Before I could answer, Laura M took my hand in hers, led me to another door, and we entered a bright cheerful room. "Oh my God," I said. "It looks like a Jolly Green Giant silver glazed donut!"

"Yes." She laughed. "And see how big the hole is? It won't be anywhere near your face. Now lie down on the platform and I'll show you how smoothly it goes up and down."

And then I heard Janine A's voice behind a large glass window. "Hi. I'm going to turn it on now so you can hear how soft the tap sounds." Lo and behold, I could barely hear it. "And," she continued, "we'll be with you the whole time."

I was sure there was a hitch somewhere. "The procedure is an hour or two. Right?"

"How much do you weigh"? she responded.

"One hundred and twenty pounds."

She then gave me one of those Janine A smiles. "Fifteen minutes. Twenty max."

We returned to the small room. I was given a quick and painless shot versus an hour IV. The room had a private bathroom, as well as a working television. It was comfortable and relaxing. Needless to say, the valium remained in my pocket.

The scan was a non-event. True to her word, Janine spoke to me often, and alerted me when an area was completed, and when I was going to move. True to her word, eighteen minutes later I was finished.

I learned several valuable lessons from this experience. The greatest lessons of all were to quit listening to others and to understand that many future events aren't anywhere near the "reality" you've been told.

Janine, me, and Laura

Rainy Days

I am a sunshine girl. I've always been at my best when the sun is shining—most energetic, most optimistic, most creative, and most full of joy. But because of my hectic life as a self-labeled Type A, I never found time to simply be. Even in retirement, my schedule was so busy I barely had a free hour for myself. That's why I always loved rainy days, especially the soft rain that I could hear patter on my roof. I thought of it as nature's version of classical music. When it rained, I enjoyed the precious free time to relax by the fire and curl up with a good book, watch a Netflix movie that had been on my list for months, or write a long, lazy entry in my journal. I waited for and savored those rainy days.

Everything changed after my lobectomy and during my chemotherapy. The world that I had so loved changed dramatically. And the place of rain in my life was one of the greatest changes of all. A gray, rainy day brought gray and gloomy moods.

I couldn't take my daily walks without getting soaked in the rain and worrying that my compromised immune system made it much easier to get sick and stay sick. Even if I could only walk the circumference of my development once a day, those walks in the sunshine had helped me feel that I was doing my part to get healthy and strong again, and that I was still part of an alive and busy world.

Fewer friends would visit when it rained. I never understood why they could visit when the sun was out but not in the rain. Their presence brought such joy to my days. They would tell me stories about where they had been, about parties or gatherings of our friends, and about visits from their families and relatives from out-of-state. It helped me to remember that social activity, people, laughter, and camaraderie would once again be in my life if I could just hang in there.

If there was rain, I couldn't sit on my front stoop and wave to neighbors out strolling, running, cycling, or walking their dogs. Our interactions had always helped me to feel part of my neighborhood, even if we only waved and smiled at each other. But no one did their normal activities in the rain.

I also couldn't enjoy long reading sessions in the back yard when it rained. That was now my replacement for the library, a quiet corner in Starbucks, or a bench in Cape Henlopen State Park. When life was normal, I had treasured the quiet moments of solitude with a good novel or book of poetry. I learned that quiet time and serenity were very important during my illness, and the rain robbed me of that.

Worst of all, when I needed to rest in my recliner, I missed watching the birds. Henry the Hummingbird had his own private dining room, but the cardinals, yellow goldfinches, song sparrows, and wrens shared a bird feeder when it wasn't raining. They entertained me for hours and brought such joy and laughter, especially when all the different species would crowd around the circular feeder and actually share space and bird seed. It always brought back the fond memory of friends who gathered every Monday night around the bar at Shuckers Happy Hour.

One can find happiness in all times and phases of life, and I certainly found that happiness on sunny days after my operation and during chemotherapy. But I must admit I was happiest when once again, having recovered from my illness, I was able to look forward to the peace and serenity I found on rainy days as well.

Raise a Hand

I was sitting by the window in Pod 1 in the infusion room at Tunnell Cancer Center. Across from me was a gentleman receiving his chemo. His daughter was keeping him company. She waved his nurse over and told her how her father was suffering from constant diarrhea.

"We've got something that should stop that problem," the nurse said, as she smiled and nodded.

I'm not sure what came over me, but I stood up and said in a probably too-loud voice, "Hey, we have a nurse over here who has something to control this gentleman's diarrhea. I'm all over that! Who wants to stand in line with me when they hand that puppy out?"

Hands went up all over the place, and voices rose all over the room.

"I'm there!"

"Count me in!"

"Bring it on!"

I looked around at the nurses sprinkled around the room. They all were trying to hide a smile or a laugh. And patients were actually smiling and laughing too, even the man and his daughter.

Sometimes the only things that get us through the toughest times are humor and laughter.

Roller Coaster Ride

At 456 feet, Kingda Ka at Six Flags Great Adventures in New Jersey is the highest roller coaster in the world. It's also the second fastest. A hydraulic launch powers riders to 128 miles per hour in 3.5 seconds. That's probably the nearest a human can feel compared to being a speeding bullet shot from a gun.

What does this have to do with chemotherapy? More than you might think! I received a chemotherapy infusion every 21 days, and had a total of 4 treatments. Dr. M, my oncologist, told me that the drugs were very harsh, with numerous side effects, some of which could potentially harm my major organs. She said it was very important that I take all of the prescription drugs as written, follow all instructions in the Beebe manual, and pay close attention to guidelines given by the oncological nursing staff. Since I had no intention of going rogue, we were both certainly on the same page.

Family and friends often asked if I felt the same from one infusion to the next. In other words, was I generally blah for the whole time I was receiving chemotherapy, or during the process, did I sometimes feel better or worse than other times?

The easiest way to describe it is to use the analogy of the Kingda Ka roller coaster, with the starting point at the top of the first major rise. For the day receiving chemotherapy and the next two to three days, I felt strong and even vibrant. I also had a pretty good appetite and felt little to no side effects. The main reason was that I had been pumped full of steroids, saline, anti-nausea drugs, and many other miscellaneous medicines to fight the initial onslaught of the raging beast called chemotherapy. But they could only give me so much of each medication or the medications themselves would become toxic to my organs.

Once those good three or four good days were over, Kingda Ka took a fierce, very fast and incredibly dramatic fall. I didn't get "kinda sick." I went from feeling as well as one can feel on chemotherapy to feeling utterly horrible. I literally experienced the difference between feeling strong and vibrant to feeling weak, frail and overall miserable. I called that period "falling into the trough." The trough normally lasted 4-5 days. And then Kingda Ka started slowly—ever so slowly—chugging back up that phenomenally high hill, a little bit at a time, at the same pace the chemo toxins left my body.

I remember calling Triage after I got my first infusion, and telling the nurse that my sister, Pamela, wanted to visit and also go to a chemotherapy session with me. I wanted her to come when I would be feeling my best.

"How long will she visit?" the nurse asked.

"She's flying in from northern New Hampshire and plans to stay 10 days," I said. "I also want to feel strong enough to ride with my wife to pick Pamela up and drop her off at the Philadelphia airport."

"Perfect!" she said. "Have her come 7 days prior to your next infusion and stay 3 days after that. That's the 10 days you will feel your best during the infusion cycle."

She was exactly right. It was like clockwork. We had a great time—went out to dinner, shopped for furniture for the new house, went to the movies, and had some fun times and great talks. It was a wonderful visit and really raised my spirits and my energy level. And the trough hit the very next day after we dropped Pamela off at the airport. Thank God for really smart nurses!

Rudy

One of my several pre-op "must haves" was a pulmonary function test. In order to have the operation, my lung functions needed to be at certain levels. I had completed one many years ago when my primary care physician at the time, knowing I had smoked for many years, wanted to test for COPD. Just the thought brought instant dread. The test was a long and arduous process. I also didn't score very well, and I swore I would never have one again. And yet, there I sat in the waiting room of the pulmonary area of Beebe Hospital.

I was remembering some of the almost impossible and exhausting exercises I endured during that first test when I heard, "Hi. I'm Rudy. I'm going to be your technician today."

As we walked down the hall, I told Rudy I had taken this test many years ago. It was really grueling for me, and the lady kept yelling at me that I should be able to do better. It was one test after another and it took a little over three hours. A couple of times I was so out of breath I almost fainted. I shared with Rudy that I didn't think I could go through that again.

By then, I was sitting in the chair where the exam would take place. Rudy had pulled his chair in front of me until our knees were touching. He took my hands in his, looked into my eyes, and said, "YOU'RE not going to do it again, Kim. WE are going to do this test, and WE will take it one step at a time. It WON'T take three hours and you have my word that you will not take a single breath—NOT A SINGLE BREATH— without me taking it with you. We'll do all of it together."

I felt so much calmer, like a heavy weight had been lifted off my shoulders. I was no longer afraid. I suddenly realized that most of my dread had probably been caused by that impatient technician who neither particularly liked me nor her job. I did remember there were some really tough breathing exercises, but Rudy sounded like he really cared, and I knew I would be okay. Plus, I had been driving air into my lungs at the gym every day for the past few months.

Rudy was a man of his word. He took every breath that I took, and we completed the whole test in two hours and five minutes. "I don't know what your prior score was, Kim, and I'm not allowed to give you the results of this one. But I will share with you that you passed with flying colors. You can have your lung operation."

I actually felt proud of myself and was greatly relieved that I could get the surgery that I so desperately needed. We did a high five gesture, and he walked me out to the elevator, pressed the button. "If you don't mind me asking, what operation are you having?"

"A lobectomy," I said.

"Who is your surgeon?"

"Dr. W," I said.

"Kim, people come from all over to have Dr. W. If you were my grandmother, my mom, my wife, or my sister, there is no one else I would want to operate on you than Dr. W."

Rudy

An additional sense of well-being flooded my body. Rudy gave me a big smile, and I responded by giving him a big hug. He held the elevator door while I entered, and he waved goodbye as it closed.

I will never forget Rudy, who took a day that I dreaded and turned it into one of my favorite memories.

Say What?

DON'T SAY (Actual Quotes)

"I'm so sorry to hear about your cancer, especially since it's lung cancer. That's a really bad one."

"It's too bad you smoked for a lot of years. I'm sure that's the cause. It's so sad you'll have to suffer with this horrible disease due to that."

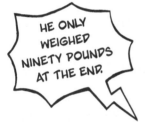

"My cousin, Bill, died of lung cancer. He only weighed ninety pounds at the end. But that was a few years ago."

"I sure hope it's not small cell lung cancer. That's really aggressive. My dad only lasted five months from diagnosis."

"My Aunt Sherry made it almost five years with lung cancer. You are younger than her so you'll probably live at least that long."

"A lady I worked with died of lung cancer. I don't know if you are going to have chemotherapy, but she did and got really, really sick. Before she died, she told me she wished she hadn't done the chemo. Just something to think about it."

SAY

"Sorry to hear about your cancer. But the drugs are so good and much improved today that I know you can do this."

"I know it's a bummer, but you are strong and tough and you have our whole Rehoboth Beach family for support. You got this and we'll be with you!!!"

"My friend, Mary, had lung cancer 15 years ago and is doing fantastic. I know you'll do great too!"

"I know there are lots of types of lung cancer. It sounds like they caught yours early. What a blessing. How can I help?"

"Promise you'll let me do something to help out. And this won't get you out of our card games you've been losing!"

"Hey, if you end up needing chemo, I would love to come to one or more of your sessions. We can play cards, talk, and just generally harass the other patients! Seriously, I'd love to help. How about it?"

Side Effects

Before I started chemotherapy, it was recommended that my spouse and I attend a four-hour class hosted by employees of Tunnell Cancer Center. We would meet several of the people who would share what we could expect over the next few months and the available services that they could provide.

I was pretty nervous and apprehensive about attending. After all, this was the building I prayed I would never have to enter. All of these years I had been so afraid of getting cancer, and now here I was, with lung cancer. 67% of my right lung had been removed, and I was almost ready to start chemotherapy.

They had a nice continental breakfast that Peg and I shared with six other new patients and their families. As we munched on the food, staff members gave each family a very professional manual to look over. It covered a variety of topics—general information and resources, appointments, test results, and information on cancer, treatment options, and wellness. Each section was reviewed by a different staff member.

By far, the longest section focused on side effects of taking chemo drugs and how to try to manage those side effects. The more they covered, the more unnerved and discouraged I became. No part of the body was spared. And sometimes each category had several side effects of its own.

- Anemia
- Appetite Changes
- Bleeding
- Constipation
- Diarrhea

- Eye Changes
- Fatigue
- Flu-Like Symptoms
- Fluid Retention
- Hair Loss
- Infection
- Infertility
- Mouth and Throat Changes
- Nausea and Vomiting
- Nervous System Changes
- Pain
- Sexual Changes
- Skin and Nail Changes
- Urinary, Kidney or Bladder Changes

The oncology nurse who was reviewing each of these general categories paused after discussing the last—Urinary, Kidney and Bladder changes. She sighed as her eyes scanned all of the participants in the room. "There is one other potential side effect that we don't print in the manual because it is a VERY rare occurrence." She grimaced.

I was thinking about our dog, Higgins. He was given a common medication for an ear infection. The vet said it was very effective but in one in every 10,000 dogs, it would cause deafness. We felt pretty good about the odds, but it turned out Higgins was the one.

I gulped as she started to speak. "It is possible that a patient might be allergic to the chemotherapy drugs as they are being infused, and can experience a mild to a very severe reaction. Possible reactions are rash, itching, flushing, changes in heart rate, low blood pressure, shortness of breath, tightening in the chest, back pain, abdominal pain, fever, and nausea. A patient who experiences a severe reaction might have a major drop in blood pressure, or even a seizure. Remember, this is very, very rare. If this occurs, we immediately stop the infusion, treat the reaction, and adjust or change the chemotherapy drugs."

Around the room, all of the eyes had the proverbial deer-in-the-headlights look, and I was sure mine were the same. You could have heard a pin drop in a room of fifteen people. "Has anyone ever died?" one brave soul spoke. "Not that I personally know of," she said, and she hurriedly packed her satchel and introduced the next speaker.

I started to wonder how I could possibly survive all of this. After all, I was almost 70. I knew they were trying to realistically prepare me for all things and give me the knowledge I needed, but I left there feeling a little frightened and anxious before the battle even began.

Slipping Back

The further I get away from my cancer journey, the more I experience moments where I start slipping back into facets of the person I was before cancer. Slipping back into thinking that I need no help or support from others, and I alone am capable of handling anything and everything that the world and life might throw my way. Slipping back into that hidden but existing arrogance, thinking that I need to be in control of anything and anyone connected with my life and often the lives of others. Slipping back into judgment mode, believing that I know what's best, and if it is not my way, it is the wrong way. Slipping back into ego trips that try to destroy my compassion, forgiveness, and serenity, forgetting the importance of connecting with other people, nature, the universe, and God.

Slipping back into who and what I was before cancer is, indeed, the most frightening experience I can imagine. So, every day that any of these aspects of my past self rear their ugly heads, I dig deep within myself until I find the light that so changed everything I was then. I close my eyes and see the faces and hear the voices that were my angels and strength and ultimate redemption from a life that I never want to live again,

Though she

be but little

she is

fierce.

-Shakespeare

from a Kim I never want to be again, and to an inner faith and connection that I never want to lose again. I use the support of Al-Anon, my Course in Miracles group, and those special village friends who "get" my struggle to continue living a benevolent life and maintaining a beloved community.

It's not always easy. It took sixty-nine years and lung cancer to find my true self. So, I forgive myself if I momentarily slip back. But I am deeply committed to working daily to maintain the person that cancer helped me to become.

Strange Bedfellows

Since I was a small child, I have had strong attachments to various people, places, and things.

Throughout the years, I have had many pets that I dearly loved. That included several dogs, cats, one little green and yellow parakeet named Yipper, and even a baby lamb called Emily.

I adored my godmother. She had polio when she was a child, walked with a crutch, and lived with my grandmother. I was named after her, and when I visited on weekends, we would bake cookies, play cards, and dress my doll.

In high school, I waited two years to get my very first guitar. My mother said I could have the S&H green stamps from grocery shopping. I was so excited when I finally got it, I named it Slick and slept with it for several months. I carried it every place I went and started a singing group at school. I also loved my first rosary. It had pink beads and a very shiny silver cross. If my clothes had a pocket, the rosary was in it.

My favorite place in the world was our camp on China Lake in Maine. We would swim, water ski, and have burgers cooked on the grill. I got to sleep on the screened-in porch and listen to the waves until they put me to sleep.

I never thought I would ever feel the same way about a port that was inserted under my skin in the left side of my chest two weeks prior to receiving chemotherapy. I really wasn't given a choice in the matter either. I was told that lung cancer drugs were very strong and harsh, and that it was easy for veins to break down by direct injection with a needle. That certainly didn't sit well with me. All I could think about was that these chemo drugs that would be shot in my veins were like the salt that causes rust build-up on a car. The salt from the winter roads could and would eat right through metal and steel. I pictured my corroded veins spurting blood and chemo drugs in all the places they shouldn't be, and somehow, I would end up in a junkyard of useless veins and body parts. I quickly decided not to question having the port.

It was also mentioned that I would require needles for many other procedures during my cancer treatment, such as blood draws, hydration sessions, IV fluids, nutrition, and dye injections for thoracic contrast CT scans. That sat even less well with me, but the doctor was certainly correct.

A port is normally removed after chemotherapy is completed. Some doctors like to leave it in for a short time after, in case additional treatment might be needed. Dr. M said it was okay to remove the port two months after I completed chemo, but I asked her if I could leave it in for a while longer. After all, I still had to have lab work completed every four months as well as contrast thoracic CT scans. They both required injections. She agreed to leave it in for a while longer.

My port has now been with me for almost a year and a half. It's not easy to wear a standard bra or wear the seat belt exactly where it should be placed. It can also hurt if I sleep on the same side as the port or lie on my belly. Even wearing a heavy sweater or jacket can cause some discomfort. I'm also very careful in the shower because I love the water very, very, hot. The port should survive this, but I'm never sure since part of it is plastic.

After my last contrast CT scan, I met with Dr. M to get the results. Two days after my appointment would mark my year anniversary of completing chemo as well as fifteen months of having the port live in my chest. As I stood up to leave, she smiled and said, "And I assume we will be leaving the port in?"

I sat back down, sighed, and said, "To be honest, Dr. M, I'm superstitious about having it removed. I'm not frightened that the procedure will hurt. I just feel that the port has been with me through this entire cancer journey, and as crazy as this sounds, I feel as if I am still receiving treatment if the port is still in my body. As long as I'm still receiving treatment, the cancer won't come back. It's like my good luck charm." I felt silly and embarrassed, listening to my own words. I teared up a bit and kept my head down. I didn't dare look at her again. She gently placed her hand on my shoulder and said, "You have no idea how many cancer patients have said the very same thing to me. It's okay. We'll leave it in." And she walked out and softly shut the door behind her.

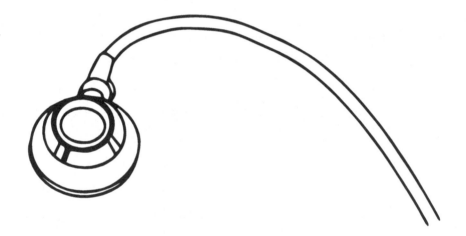

I know that sooner or later I must have the port removed. It certainly isn't the same as being attached to a person, a place, or a pet. But after all, we have been through a long journey together and have become quite attached to each other. So, for right now, I want us to remain strange bedfellows.

P.S. It is now two and a half years since I finished chemotherapy, and I still have my port. Maybe soon I will have it removed.

The Ten Commandments of Cancer

I
Thou shalt get a low-dose CT scan if you have been a smoker or been around secondhand smoke.

II
Thou shalt get all cancer screenings recommended by your doctor.

III
Thou shalt be calm and serene while awaiting test results.

IV
Thou shalt never go to appointments alone when receiving test results or diagnoses.

V
Thou shalt listen only to medical professionals regarding tests and prognosis.

VI
Thou shalt create a mantra to say when you are frightened, weak, weary, or ill.

VII
Thou shalt create a village who can respond to your various moods, needs, and ups & downs.

VIII
Thou shalt embrace thy religious or spiritual support to bolster your heart, soul, attitude, and immune system.

IX
Thou shalt engage in all activities that make you happy and joyful.

X
Thou shalt not listen to naysayers or statistics. You are not a statistic and nothing can decide your fate but you.

thrive (v.)

c. 1200, from a Scandinavian source akin to Old Norse *þrifask* "to thrive," originally "grasp to oneself," probably reflexive of *þrifa* "to clutch, grasp, grip, take hold of" (compare Norwegian *triva* "to seize," Swedish *trifvas*, Danish trives "to thrive, flourish"), of unknown origin. Related: *Thrived (or throve); thriving.*

Full Definition of *thrive*

intransitive verb

1: to grow vigorously: FLOURISH

2: to gain in wealth or possessions: PROSPER

3: to progress toward or realize a goal despite or because of circumstances—often used with *"on,"* as in "thrives on conflict"

TRIAGE at Tunnell Cancer Center

There were many worrisome times during my seven months of living with cancer. But the triage nurses at Beebe's Tunnell Cancer Center were especially diligent during my months of chemotherapy. As I left treatment, they would always say, "If anything doesn't seem right, if you feel at all sick or even different, make sure to call us at Triage and we'll work through it with you." They encouraged me to take my temperature and blood pressure daily, monitor both my eating and bathroom habits, and be aware of anything that seemed unusual or different from the norm. When I would call, I would hear, "There is nothing that is too minor to call about, and there is no such thing as a stupid question." I would hear this from every nurse every time I called, and I would feel accepted and important.

So, I called. I called when my normal 110 blood pressure was 150. I called when my constant 97.7 temperature was 99.9. I called when the nausea medication didn't last quite as long as it should. I called when my tongue turned white and I had a hard time swallowing.

I called, and I called, and I called. And not once, not a single time, did any nurse make me feel silly or stupid. Not one nurse ever got irritated with me, even if they had to explain their answer more than once. Every time I called, whatever nurse answered would always calmly ask me

a question or two, explain to me exactly what was going on, and then tell me how we would fix it together. Even today, I call Triage regarding appointments or certain tests or seeking their opinion about a medical decision I must make.

I will always feel deep gratitude to each and every triage nurse who made a difficult and scary situation so much better. Because they would fix whatever was wrong, I could feel unafraid and confident again.

Tsunami Waves

A tsunami is a series of ocean waves caused by an underwater earth-quake, landslide, or volcanic eruption. The first wave is usually not the strongest, but successive waves grow bigger and stronger and wreak more havoc and destruction as they move toward their final destination.

Chemotherapy produces its own tsunami waves. Each successive infusion normally causes more side effects, and existing side effects get worse as the treatments increase, resulting in a cumulative and strong negative attack on the body.

For some reason, thinking of chemotherapy treatments as if they were a series of tsunami waves really helped me mentally, physically, and perhaps even spiritually. I knew what to expect. I watched friends and family before me live through the effects of chemotherapy, and knowing the possibility of what I might face made the journey easier. Seeing others survive its ravages gave me strength, hope, and courage.

Yes, chemotherapy treatments were inevitable, but life is full of choic-es, and I made mine prior to starting treatment. I chose:

- not to anticipate or assume it would destroy much of
  my body
- not to get lost in its immensity before it even happened
- not to tense up and cower in fear before I experienced it
- to go with the flow of the treatments
- to go to treatments with a positive attitude, courage,
  and love
- to explicitly follow the directions of my doctors and
  nursing staff, and to take the countless medications
  exactly as prescribed

I was very fortunate. There were some tough days, but not half as many as I thought. I also received a wonderful gift. The last treatment is always the worst, and when my fourth and last treatment approached, even the most positive infusion and triage nurses gently told me to batten down the hatches and prepare for a very difficult ride. My third infusion had been tough, but I rode that wave, and I made up my mind I would ride this one too.

Interestingly, my fourth infusion was the easiest and most gentle. Maybe because I had prepared for the worst. Maybe because my spirits were so high that this was the last treatment. Or just maybe, sometimes when we least expect it, the universe gives us a gift.

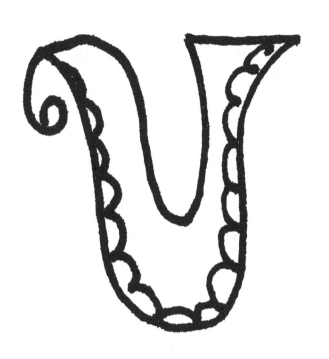

Unflappable

In my youth, I was strong, bold, and adventurous. I was unflappable in the face of challenges. These traits helped me to succeed in school as well as in business.

As I grew and had more interaction with the "world," however, those positive traits got intertwined with my ego, and I became arrogant, controlling, and judgmental. I neither needed nor accepted anything from anyone. I had it "covered."

Then I got cancer, and I had to make a major decision. Did I face and fight cancer with more of the Kim I had become in the last 69 years, or call forth the traits of my youth and be assertive, yet positive and calm?

I knew in my heart that there was only one way to go. I chose to reach out to others for help and support. I believe the route I chose literally saved my life. People, prayers, and light flooded my world and made the journey so much easier.

Kim's Journey

To this day, I remind myself every morning that I have a choice of who I want to be. That choice is the Kim who returned once I had cancer.

Unspoken Word

Dr. B, Primary Care Physician (Phone)

"I have the results of your low-dose CT scan, and there is a 1.3 centimeter spiculated nodule on your right lung and an enlarged lymph node in the middle of your chest. I'm going to refer you to a pulmonologist to read the scan and determine next steps."

"Do you think it's **CANCER?**"

"It's hard to tell. Some spiculated nodules are, some aren't. It normally depends on size. And some enlarged lymph nodes are dangerous and some are not."

"Are my spiculated nodule and lymph node big?"

"I've seen bigger. The doctor will probably first either biopsy or aspirate the nodule to determine more clearly what it is and then deal with the lymph node."

Dr. K, Pulmonologist (Office)

"If you look right here at the scan, you can see the nodule and right over here is the lymph node. Our normal course of action is to either aspirate or biopsy the nodule to determine exactly what we are dealing with. But because we also have the enlarged lymph node, just to be on the safe side, I would like to send you for a PET scan to make sure there are no other lesions on other organs of your body. Then we'll take it from there."

"Do you think I have **CANCER?**"

"Let's get the PET scan and go from there."

Dr. K, Pulmonologist (Phone)

"Good news. There are no other lesions in your body and the lymph node is fine. But we need to treat the nodule aggressively. I've already referred you for an appointment with a thoracic surgeon."

"Do you think it's **CANCER?**"

"It's hard to tell. Dr. W will interpret the PET scan for you."

Dr. W, Thoracic Surgeon (Office)

"Do you see how this whole screen is dark except for this one area that is lit up like a Christmas tree? That is what I will take out."

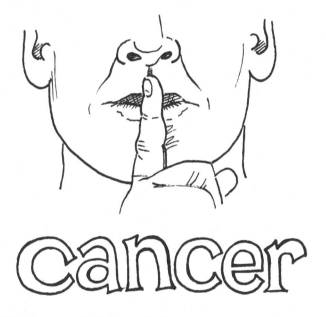

I didn't bother to ask if the nodule was cancerous. I was on my third doctor and fourth conversation, and I realized that cancer was and would remain the unspoken word until some pathologist in a chemistry lab was absolutely positive that my nodule was NOT normal and I had cancer. I understood their caution and perhaps even legal restrictions, but the process was terribly frustrating and exasperating. It was always the elephant not only in the room but in my mind twenty-four hours a day until the "fat pathologist sang" that yes, indeed, I had cancer.

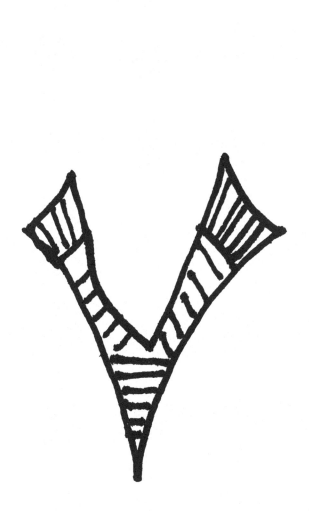

Victory Laps

I spent four days in ICU after my lobectomy operation. That's an unusually long time for standard lung surgery, and it was three days more than the doctor wanted. For some reason, the fluid in my chest was not draining as quickly as he wished.

The ICU floor was a perfect square, and on the morning of day two I decided I would be a prime example of how God helps those who help themselves, chest tube and all. I sweet-talked my favorite nurse, Jen, into allowing me to take a little excursion. She helped me out of bed, made sure all my IV paraphernalia was properly attached to the portable stand, had me hold the chest tube so it wouldn't hit anything along the way and inadvertently rip out of my chest, and then put on my skid-proof slippers. I felt like a football or hockey player all suited up for the big game. The IV stand was on wheels and helped to give me leverage and balance. Off I went! I kept my eyes straight ahead and was extremely careful taking each step. I didn't look in any patient rooms or converse with nurses behind the main desk or walking in the hallway. I was on a mission and it had my full attention.

On the first trip, I completed the perimeter twice. I was going for a third, but Jen said I was looking peaked and was swaying a bit. It was exhilarating! I felt like I had run a 10k race and was back in control of

Jen

my destiny. I begged for a repeat run mid-afternoon, and Jen being Jen, readied me again. In the evening of day two, I completed my third trip and was up to six laps.

On the third day, I was up and ready to start my laps at 7:30 A.M. Jen gave me the "good to go" thumbs up, and I was off. Day three was a different experience. I was stronger and much more confident. By the third lap I started looking at my surroundings—in the rooms, at the nursing station, and at hospital workers and visitors walking in the hallway. All seemed to give me strange looks. I finally realized that people didn't usually get out of bed or do laps on the ICU floor.

By the fourth lap, I was the main attraction. I heard a nurse say to another nurse, "I'll lay you five she gets up to twelve laps by the end of our shift." I started hearing clapping and "go girl," "you can do it," and "do one for me" coming from some of the rooms. I saw waving hands, big smiles, and gestures of thumbs up not only from patients but from nurses, workmen, and visitors in the hallway.

I suddenly realized I was not alone. I wasn't walking just for myself. There were others walking with me. The man in 3 with stage 4 COPD. The woman fighting sepsis in 6. The college student in 11 with advanced pneumonia. And the grandmother in 14 with severe complications of diabetes. I felt their spirits lift my own. I knew that we were all one and struggling for the same goal…life. By the end of the day we—me, patients, ICU nurses, hospital workers, and visitors—completed fifteen laps. It remains one of the greatest victories of my life.

Village Strong

I learned that the toughest parts of cancer weren't operations, chemo-therapy, constant needle jabs for lab work, scans, or continual trips to doctors and the pharmacy. The toughest parts of cancer were the emotional, psychological, and spiritual ups and downs. It was being on top of the world one day when a victory occurred, and the next day being in a dark abyss when it didn't go as well as hoped. Or sometimes it was just the reality that I had lung cancer that hit me like a two by four.

Every day was unique and came with new surprises. Situations and moods were scattered, inconsistent and diverse. I knew that I had an incredibly supportive family and stellar friends. There was the "hood," of course. Close friends I saw often for card parties, dinners, birthdays, and happy hours. And in the beach town where I lived, there was the "almost-hood." These friends were always present at larger parties, like weddings, holiday gatherings, and concerts. So, I saw them pretty often.

I even had the "run-into-a-lot-but-don't-hang-with-a-lot-hood." These were friends I might see at the grocery store or Panera or go with for a coffee or drink to catch up.

They all added such joy and light in my life during my illness. There were also the awesome members from my UU church, and various groups I belonged to and loved—Al-Anon, A Course in Miracles, Rehoboth Beach Writers Guild, Hand and Foot card group, the Coastal Camera Club, UU book club, and the Cycling Club. And last but certainly not least, were the people I reached out to in one of my many vulnerable moments—a Beebe office worker or technician, the appointment coordinator in Dr. B's office, the customer in line at the bank. All of these people then told their families, friends, and members of their churches and groups about me and my struggle.

As time went on, my village became a town and then a city and then a metropolis and then a state and then a country and then a world and then a universe filled with love, prayers, energy, and good thoughts. Its power raised me above the daily ups and downs, worries, fears and uncertainties, and replaced them with a peace, serenity, and positivity beyond anything I had ever experienced and probably ever will again.

Vulnerability

I used to think
that if I was vulnerable,
I was weak.
Through my journey,
I learned that it takes
      courage
            and strength
to be vulnerable.

Waiting

I felt like I was constantly waiting. Waiting to meet with new doctors. Waiting to meet the same new doctors for follow-up visits. Waiting for tests, procedures, scans, and lab work. Waiting for the results of tests, procedures, scans, and lab work. Waiting to find out next steps. Waiting to find out the significance and results of those next steps. Waiting to get prescriptions filled. Waiting on hold for the doctor's office to answer so I could tell them the pharmacy couldn't find the prescriptions. Waiting in line to pick up the prescriptions. Waiting for the exact right time to take the drugs. Waiting to get prescriptions re-filled. And just when I would think I had the whole waiting thing under control—BAM— someone, someplace, or something would change, and I would have to follow a new path. And that always required more waiting.

I learned early in the process that cancer requires the patience of a saint and the analytical skills of an engineer. The business of cancer became a full-time job. And so much of that job required waiting.

I am not a patient person. If you haven't placed your foot on the gas pedal three seconds after the light turns green, I'm one of those obnoxious people who will lay on her horn. I try so hard NOT to be that person, but it takes all of my will power to wait patiently for anything.

Hard as it was, I struggled to find patience through the whole cancer journey, especially waiting for the day that Dr. M told me my latest CT scan showed no cancer. That was a statement worth waiting for!

Which One?

I believe that we face all of the ups and downs of life one of two ways—with a foundation of fear or a foundation of love.

Which carries more weight?

I CHOSE LOVE

Will

I can awaken every morning filled with thanks and gratitude for being alive...

I can release fear and anxiety and any darkness that tries to cloud my light...

I can live each day striving to be my best self and welcoming the love and prayers of others...

I can...so I will.

Where's

FINDING Books AND PUZZLES

9 a.m. Visiting nurse

Carol

10 a.m. phone call ≈
1 pm. Dr. W

✓ with pharmacy

2:30 p.m. Sue & Marty
5:00 p.m.

going with me on boring walks

bringing me a cool water

AT CVS

MAKING SPECIAL
TREATS

sitting with me at chemo

TAKING ME FOR CAR RIDES

searching for shows

my wife ? ? ?

cooking

picking up meds

paying cable bill

walking dog

ANSWERING PHONE

helping me bathe and dress

DRIVING ME TO APPOINTMENTS

sitting in ICU room for hours

filling bird feeder

Grocery shopping

milk
eggs
juice
p.butter

tiptoeing around while

doing laundry

COOKING

sleep

Wonders of Reiki

Reiki is based on the belief that the body has an energy field that can affect a person's health and happiness. The goal of Reiki is to restore the balance of that energy so it supports all physical and spiritual aspects of our lives.

My dear friend, Maria, offered to practice daily Reiki on me after my lung operation and while I was receiving chemotherapy. I gladly accepted, but I was puzzled when she told me that she could perform the practice remotely. I thought Reiki was a hands-on procedure where universal energy transfers directly from the palms of the practitioner into the body of the receiver.

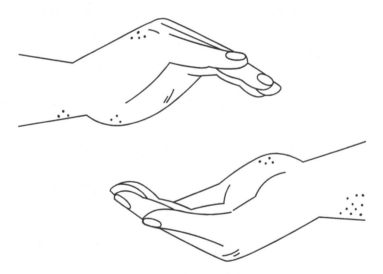

"Are you familiar with chakras?" she said.

"Yes," I said. "They're energy wheels located in the body that correspond to nerve bundles and major organs."

"Right," she said. "Your job is to always keep those chakras open so you can accept the universal energy."

"Why? Will you direct the energy to my chakras and then help me be healthy and well?"

"I'm going to tell you the truth, Kim. My only job is to send universal energy to you."

She explained that I must choose to believe in and receive that energy. If I did, it would enter my chakras, and I could direct it toward whatever I needed or wanted to heal—physical, emotional, mental, or spiritual problems. Ultimately, she was simply the conduit. I was the healer.

I am convinced that my acceptance and belief in Reiki's energy and healing power affected both my physical response to cancer as well as my level of peace and serenity throughout the experience.

Sometimes, I think it's just a matter of opening our minds (and our chakras) to all the miracles of the universe.

maria

X Marks the Lobectomy Spot

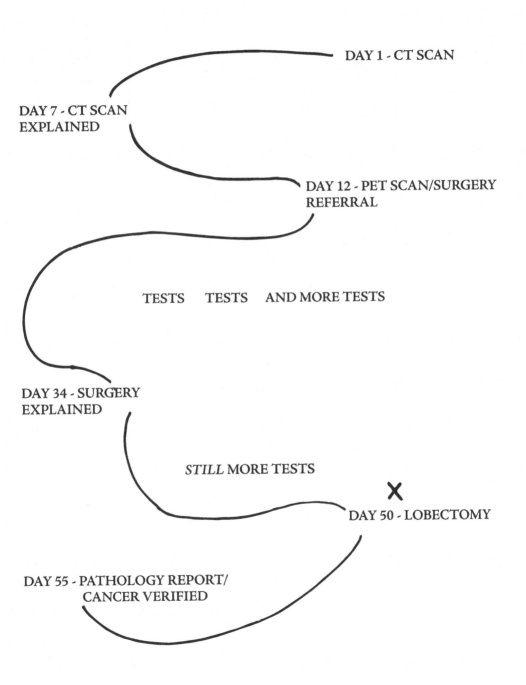

DAY 1 - CT SCAN

DAY 7 - CT SCAN
EXPLAINED

DAY 12 - PET SCAN/SURGERY
REFERRAL

TESTS   TESTS   AND MORE TESTS

DAY 34 - SURGERY
EXPLAINED

STILL MORE TESTS

X

DAY 50 - LOBECTOMY

DAY 55 - PATHOLOGY REPORT/
CANCER VERIFIED

X-rays and Scans

SCAN	Full Name	How it Works	What it Does
Low-dose CT	Low-dose Computed Tomography Scan	Takes a series of X-rays from different angles	Detects lung abnormalities as small as a grain of rice
Traditional CT	Computed Tomography Scan	Takes a series of X-rays from different angles and creates cross-sectional slices of bones, blood vessels, and soft tissues	Detects tumors, investigates internal bleeding, checks for other internal injuries or damage
Contrast CT	Contrast Computed Tomography Scan	Uses a special dye which highlights the part of the body being examined. Takes a series of X-rays from different angles and creates cross-sectional slices of bones, blood vessels, and soft tissues	Detects tumors and other abnormalities Shows a cleaner and more detailed picture than a regular CT scan
PET scan	Positron Emission Tomography	Uses an injectable, mildly radioactive drug to show where cells are more active than normal	Detects early signs of cancer, brain disorders, and heart disease
MRI	Magnetic Resonance Imaging	Uses a strong magnetic field, radio waves, and a computer to create a detailed cross-sectional image of internal organs and structures	Detects brain tumors, traumatic injury, multiple sclerosis, stroke, dementia, infection, and developmental abnormalities

YOU WILL DIE

I met Debbie D, my spiritual advisor whom I discussed in *Only a Memory*, at dinner after a Sunday matinee at Clear Space Theatre. We sat across from one another, and I overheard her telling someone that she helped ease the journey for people transitioning from life to death.

I instinctively knew that this "chance" meeting was not by chance. It was meant to happen. So, I joined the conversation. We talked for a good forty-five minutes about the spirit world, God, life and death, and passing from one world to another. It was a fascinating exchange, and the more we talked, the more connected and comfortable I felt with this woman. I finally found the courage to say, "Debbie, I think I may have to employ your services." She looked at me intently and replied," I think we need to have a private conversation." We agreed to meet that Sunday at a popular local diner.

When I arrived, she already had a table. As soon as I sat down, we started talking.

"Why do you think you will need my services? Do you have a terminally ill relative or partner?"

"No. I've just been diagnosed with lung cancer. I know that it's a really terrible cancer, and every year it's the leading cause of all cancer deaths." I looked down at the table. I didn't want her to see the fear and dread I knew must be showing in my eyes

"Kim, I think there is something we need to get out of the way up front." She took my hands in hers, leaned forward and said, "Look at me," and I did. "You are going to die, Kim. You need to understand this up front. You are going to die."

I was filled with terror and trepidation. I imagined my ashes in a mahogany urn with a framed 5 x 7 photo of me sitting in front of it. I even knew which photo I had asked Peg to select. Why didn't she have the drug store make an 8 x 10? I wondered. I could see people filing by and making the meaningless remarks we all make when we go to a funeral. "What a nice smile." "She looks full of life in that photo." "I bet she was a bit younger there, don't you think?" I imagined a woman I didn't even know picking up my photo and studying it, touching the frame to make sure it was wood, not plastic. I felt violated by her action and was angry at this stranger's intimacy with my image. Debbie was still silent. This all flashed in my mind in what felt like just a few seconds. I looked up at her, knowing she had given me the time to live my own death.

She continued to stare at me intently, letting her words sink in. Finally, she said, "We are ALL going to die, Kim. Only God knows how. Only God knows when. Only God can determine your journey. No one has a free pass. No one can choose the day or time or cause. You may die on your way home from this meeting. You may live another twenty years. If you can accept that you are going to die—that your death is inevitable—we can get that out of the way, and we can focus on you living, and on you thriving throughout this journey you are about to take."

From that day on, Debbie became my spiritual advisor and dear friend. Throughout my cancer journey, we met regularly on Sundays at the Ocean Grill Diner. There were many things we discussed and worked through during those challenging weeks and months. But fear of dying was never again one of them.

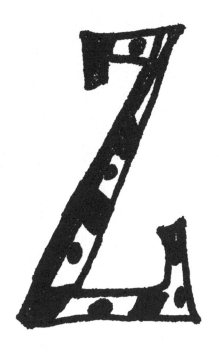

Zip It

Throughout this memoir, I have touched upon some very difficult moments and periods of time during my cancer experience. Those times were especially true when I first learned that I had lung cancer and needed a lobectomy. Some days were so dark that I thought I would suffocate in their impenetrable blackness. I was desperately trying to wrap my head around how my life could take such a dramatic and profound turn in just an instant. The realization of my mortality was pervasive and overwhelming.

My mind, body and soul were simply numb. I tried to think but couldn't. I tried to feel but couldn't. I tried to connect to my spirit and my God but couldn't. I felt like I was endlessly floating and had no rudder or control. I would walk and talk but I innately knew my essence wasn't there. I kept searching for some sort of anchor—something, someone, some place that could ground me in this new and daunting reality I must live.

Of all those initial dark times, the irony was that the most fear and anxiety I experienced was caused by people who wanted nothing more than to connect with me and to make me feel better. The way they invariably attempted to do that, however, was by relating in the only way they knew how—sharing cancer stories of others they knew. And the majority of those stories were of pain, suffering, the horror of chemotherapy, the ravages of lung cancer, how long their loved one lasted, and what they weighed when they died. They imparted advice that I might want to consider, and so many other things that I neither wanted nor needed to know.

"Zip it!" I wanted to tell them. They meant well, but it wasn't working.

There's no perfect thing to say to someone who has cancer. There's also no easy out by saying nothing. But I think I can speak for most folks who have cancer when I tell you that is it FAR more important what you don't say than what you do.

Some people with cancer want to talk about their cancer. Others do not. Asking an open-ended question gives an opportunity for the person to make a choice. How are you feeling? How are you doing? The good news is that the conversation is now focused on the person who has cancer and who either does or doesn't want to talk about it.

Cancer is also a full-time job at a time when most folks are sick and weak and unable to complete all the necessary tasks associated with their cancer. There are countless doctors' appointments, chemotherapy sessions, tests, procedures, prescriptions, special foods, and over-the-counter medicines to purchase, and so many other small errands and tasks—all that are over and above the regular errands and duties of living. A sincere "Please tell me how I can help" will open the door for the person to ask for support if they want or need it. You might even give some examples of how you would like to help, i.e., bring them to doctor's appointments, go with them to chemotherapy, grocery shop, visit and chat, make soup, pick up prescriptions, etc. This assures them you really want to help and gives them the chance to tell you what they would like.

And if you have or get cancer, try to be kind, and understand that people are doing the best they can. They are connecting in the only way they know how. In turn, cut them short from any negative stories and gruesome examples with a smile, a glance at your watch, and a polite "I need to go." It is imperative that you stay in the light, strong, and serene. Don't let anyone rain on your goals of health and mental well-being. This is YOUR journey...and you will thrive!

Fabulous Family

Peg, me, Pam, Ed

Back Row: Peter, Allen
Front Row: Cindy, me, Pam

 me & Peg at our wedding

Peg & Higgins

Patti & Charles

Patti, Peg & michael

Higgins

me & Peg

Cindy & Jeff

Dee & Allen

Jake & Higgins

me & Jake

Sadie, Ella, Tina, Jim, & Jack

Peg & me

Higgins

me, Pam, & Cindy

Angel
Friends

Alice

Ellie

Ruth

mary

John

Carol

Elise, Joyce, Deb, & Lo

Tony

Amanda

Jan

Bonnie, Darlene, Jean & me

Don

Caryl

Sue

Carol

Jeanne & Sheryl

Part of H.S. Class of '67

Karen

Roy

Joan

Epilogue

From the time I was a little girl, I was afraid of cancer. I wrote an essay in this book entitled "Dread" that described how deeply I hated the look, the sounds, and the smell of cancer. Bare-headed people with sunken eyes and flaccid skin, either strapped to IV poles or struggling to push their wheelchairs. Everything about cancer deeply frightened me.

All that changed when I got cancer. I was no longer frightened, and I gradually felt a part of a greater world of wonderful human beings struggling to rise above their adversities, and living with light and hope, no matter what the odds.

In the middle of writing *Thriving*, a new fear was born. COVID 19 swept over our country like a massive tsunami wave, leaving no innocents in its path. There were no counter-acting drugs or shots at the beginning. There was no firm guidance and research to count on. And all we could do was wear masks, wipe everything down with an alcohol-based product, and stay away from others.

Those were the days of Delta, and my doctors made it clear that between my age, missing 67% of one of my lungs, my COPD, and a compromised immune system, I would struggle to survive it. Consequently, loving, caring friends ran our errands, bought our groceries, etc. We were totally isolated and went nowhere and saw no people. I was petrified that I would catch it and die.

As I write this epilogue I have already received two shots and two boosters, and we are now fighting Omicron and its variants. Since it is highly contagious but far milder, the rules have dramatically loosened, and people have been encouraged to wear N95 masks and go about living their lives. This summer, my wife and I finally felt safe enough to follow all rules and go on a trip. We enjoyed an absolutely lovely Viking river cruise. The day before we landed home, I didn't feel well.

A long story short, yes……..I tested positive for COVID. Here it was. The thing I so dreaded and feared would be my demise. Once I was diagnosed, however, my fear and anxiety dissipated, and I took a deep breath and knew I could handle this. I was blessed with an extremely mild case and had a bit of lingering fatigue and am now doing very well.

There is a moral I want to share in this epilogue. I spent so many hours, days, weeks, months, and yes, even years being anxious and frightened about things that I could neither control nor prevent in my life. I finally understood in these last few years that what I really feared was fear. I allowed fear to rule so very much of my life. Perhaps it is later than I would like, but I have finally realized that I need to simply live one day at a time, to breathe the air, smile at the sun, walk barefoot in the grass, kiss and hug my animals, appreciate and love my wife, cherish my family and friends, and remember something my mother told me almost sixty years ago: "Honey, you can't take one more breath than God wants you to take, and you have to take every breath that He does give you. So just enjoy the life you have been given."

Acknowledgments

To Ellen Collins, my editor and mentor, for her wonderful ideas, her creative suggestions that so improved the book, her contribution of three beautiful poems, her line art for many of the essays, and the hours and hours she spent helping me to express the messages I wanted to share.

To Kathleen Fitzgerald, my friend and artist, who dedicated her time and incredible talent creating the cover art, art interpretation of the poems, and line art for several of the essays. She spent many hours producing different versions of each piece and was always so caring and upbeat about this project. I am so very grateful to her and all that she added to this book.

To Crystal Heidel, owner and founder of Byzantium Sky Press, LLC, who added so much of her expertise that went far beyond book set-up. Her ideas, advice, suggestions, improvements, and creativity created a wonderful additional dimension of my vision for this book. Her help and support were invaluable.

To my wonderful brother-in-law Jeff Clapperton, who rode the highways of Maine in the middle of winter, searching for a white birch tree that was basically growing out of stone and a few grains of sand....and was still thriving. The photograph he took was the inspiration Kathleen used for the book's cover.

Made in USA - Kendallville, IN
13409_9798218114039
01.05.2023 1652